GCSE Statistics
Higher Workbook

This book is for anyone doing GCSE Statistics at Higher Level.

This book contains lots of tricky questions designed
to make you sweat — because that's
the only way you'll get better.

It's also got some daft bits in to try and make the whole
experience at least vaguely entertaining for you.

What CGP is all about

Our sole aim here at CGP is to produce the highest quality
books — carefully written, immaculately presented and
dangerously close to being funny.

Then we work our socks off to get them
out to you — at the cheapest possible prices.

Contents

Section One — Data Collection

Section Two — Tabulation and Representation

Section Three — Data Analysis

Section Four — Probability

Published by Coordination Group Publications Ltd.

Editors:
Charlotte Burrows, David Hickinson, Delene Kang, Alison Palin.

Contributors:
Andrew Ballard, Sally Gill, Val Malcolm, Nova Thornley and Janet West.

Proofreading:
Alastair Duncombe and Andy Park.

ISBN: 978 1 84146 414 5

Groovy website: www.cgpbooks.co.uk
Printed by Elanders Hindson Ltd, Newcastle upon Tyne.
Jolly bits of clipart from CorelDRAW®

Based on the classic CGP style created by Richard Parsons.

Planning an Investigation

 Flash, bang, whizzzzzz... Wooo. Welcome to the GCSE Stats workbook. The first topic to sink your teeth into is planning an investigation. You need to be able to think of a <u>hypothesis</u> for your investigation — this will <u>explain</u> clearly what you think is <u>going to happen</u>.

Q1 A head teacher wants to investigate how the exam timetable affects how well the students in her school do in exams. Write down two sub-questions that she could ask.

Q2 Rod, Jane and Eddie are playing a card game. Rod and Jane think that Eddie is cheating by stacking the deck because he has won 9 games out of 10. State a hypothesis that Rod and Jane could test to investigate their theory that Eddie is cheating.

Q3 The Fixit drug company have discovered a new drug which they call "Poxfix". They think that Poxfix could be a cure for chickenpox. What hypothesis should the Fixit drug company test to see if Poxfix works?

Q4 A sports scientist thinks that the more TV students watch, the more likely they are to be overweight and do badly in exams. State two hypotheses that the scientist should test to see if he is right.

Q5 Last year, in the middle of summer, the Freezee ice cream company ran a leafleting campaign to promote their products. They wanted to test the hypothesis: *The campaign increased sales of ice creams per day*.

	Average number of ice creams sold per day
Before leafleting campaign	486
After leafleting campaign	687

Using the data in the table what conclusion can you draw about Freezee's hypothesis? Give a reason for your answer.

Q6 Mrs Counter the statistics teacher thinks that when her students attend extra revision classes after school, their performance at Statistics GCSE improves.

a) What hypothesis should Mrs Counter test to investigate the effectiveness of the revision classes?

A student in Mrs Counter's class investigates the results of last year's GCSE. He finds that, in general, students who didn't attend the extra classes got higher grades than those who did.

b) Give one reason why this could have happened.

Data Sources

Remember, first you need to decide whether it's best to get your data from a primary or secondary source. Then you need to decide how to collect your data. Decisions, decisions.

Q1 Say whether each of these data collection methods gives primary or secondary data.

a) Using data from the 1901 census.

b) Doing an experiment to see how long students take to complete a puzzle.

c) Using temperature charts from a national newspaper.

Q2 In 2005 the Wonderme cosmetics company claimed that its anti-wrinkle cream was more effective than any other on the market. In 2009 a beauty salon used the Wonderme statistics when deciding which anti-wrinkle cream to promote.

a) Is the data used by the beauty salon primary or secondary data?

b) Give two disadvantages of using these statistics.

Remember — you collect primary data; someone else collects secondary data.

Q3 Complete the table by saying whether the data is primary or secondary.

Data	Primary or Secondary
You use data from the 2001 census on the number of rooms in a house.	
You use results from your experiment measuring sizes of spider webs.	
You use a pie chart from a magazine showing preferred beauty products.	
You use a grouped frequency table compiled by a supermarket showing the number of times customers visit the supermarket each month.	

Q4 A market research company collects data on the amount spent on clothes per week by all the people living on Rosamund Street. The table below shows the ages of the people interviewed.

Age	Under 18	18-30	31-45	46-60	Over 60
Frequency	2	13	12	20	53

Cuthbert finds the company's data when he is doing research on how school children spend their pocket money.

a) Is this primary or secondary data?

b) Give one reason why Cuthbert should not use this data.

Remember, your sources have to be relevant, accurate and unbiased.

Q5 Phloggit Advertising have compiled a graph to show how they have improved the sales figures of their client, Swindluz Sweets. Kate is thinking about showing the data in the graph as a bar chart for her business studies project on marketing methods.

a) Give one criticism of this piece of data.

b) Say whether the graph is primary or secondary data.

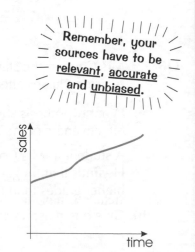

Data Sources

Q6 The makers of Raz washing powder want to test the hypothesis:

Clothes cleaned with Raz washing powder are whiter than clothes cleaned with any other brand.

How could the makers of Raz test this hypothesis?

After you've made a hypothesis you're going to have to figure out what data to collect and how you're going to collect it.

Q7 The management of a boy band want to find out if their assumptions about members of the band's fan club are true. They decide to test this hypothesis:

The majority of fan club members are girls aged between 7 and 13.

I'm such a fan of boy bands.

a) Would you use a primary or secondary source of data? Explain your answer.

b) How could the management of the band collect data to test their hypothesis?

Q8 Students at a school are doing a project on recycling in their local area. They decide to test the hypothesis:

Recycling levels rose after the council set up a collection service.

a) Do you think they should use primary or secondary data to test the hypothesis? Give a reason for your answer.

b) Describe one way in which the students could test the hypothesis.

Q9 A health authority is concerned about the sale of sweets and crisps in 10 schools. They think that this could lead to higher numbers of overweight students. One piece of data the health authority needs to find out is the weights of students in the 10 schools.

a) What second piece of data is needed to test the hypothesis?

b) For each piece of data, should the health authority use primary or secondary data? Give reasons for your answers.

c) What method of data collection should the local authority use to find out the weights of the students? Give a reason for your answer.

Q10 Adam is investigating how age affects car insurance prices. He collects primary data by checking the insurance companies' websites and secondary data from a motoring magazine.

a) Suggest one advantage of him collecting primary data.

b) Suggest one advantage of him using a motoring magazine as a source for his data.

Q11 The local council wants to investigate whether or not road traffic accidents at a certain junction are more likely to occur during the morning rush hour (between 8 a.m and 9 a.m.) than any other time of day.

a) What data does the local council need to collect?

b) Should the local council use primary or secondary data? Give a reason for your answer.

c) Suggest a method that the local council could use.

Types of Data

 Data can be qualitative or quantitative. And quantitative data can be discrete or continuous — know the differences.

Q1 **a)** Write down a definition of quantitative data.

  b) What is the name given to data which can't be measured numerically?

Q2 Zac collects some data about his school. The data items are listed below. Say whether each data item is qualitative or quantitative.

  a) The colours of pants worn by the teachers.

  b) The number of students late to school from each form on the first day of term.

  c) The distance travelled to school by each student.

  d) The star sign of each student.

Q3 **a)** What name is given to quantitative data that can be measured exactly?

  b) Give one example of this type of data.

  c) Write down a definition of continuous data.

  d) Give one example of continuous data.

Q4 A music shop sells CDs, DVDs, tapes and some vinyl records.

  a) State one example of qualitative data that could be collected by the shop.

  b) State one example of quantitative data that could be collected by the shop.

Q5 Amy collects some data at her school sports day. The data items are listed below. Say whether each data item is discrete or continuous.

  a) The number of competitors in each event.

  b) The finishing times of each competitor in the 100-metre sprint.

  c) The total number of points scored by each form at the end of the day.

  d) The distances jumped by each competitor in the long jump.

Q6 **a)** What is bivariate data?

  Say whether the data described below is discrete bivariate data or continuous bivariate data.

  b) Shoe size and marks out of 20 scored in a science test.

  c) Heights and tail lengths of lesser spotted ferrets.

Classifying Data

Loads and loads of data can be pretty hard to analyse, so it helps to group it together to make it more manageable. All I can say is that it leads to one classy page...

Q1 The table shows the number of coins in the pockets of a random sample of 100 people.

Number of coins	0-5	6-10	11-15	16-30
Frequency	44	26	19	11

a) What are the lower class boundaries?

b) What are the class intervals in the table?

Q2 Fred asked each of his 30 classmates how long (to the **nearest minute**) it took them to eat their dinner. Here are the results he recorded:

42	13	3	31	15	20	19	1	59	14
8	25	16	27	4	55	32	31	31	10
32	17	16	19	29	42	43	30	29	18

a) Copy and complete the table by grouping the data appropriately.

b) State one disadvantage of grouping data.

Length of time (mins)						
Number of people						

Q3 a) Write down a definition of a categorical scale of measurement.

b) The owner of a fast food restaurant collects data on the types of burgers sold in a week. The data is recorded in the table below.

Type of burger	Frequency
1	276
2	314
3	181
4	189

Key
1 – Hamburger
2 – Cheese burger
3 – Chicken burger
4 – Vegetarian burger

i) What type of scale of measurement is the owner using?

ii) In the table, hamburgers are labelled 1 and cheeseburgers are labelled 2. Does this mean cheese burgers are twice as good as hamburgers?

Q4 Ben is collecting data about the clothes people are buying. He splits the clothes into five classes — nice clothes, OK clothes, rubbish clothes, only-fit-for-the-bin clothes, and shoes.

a) Give one criticism of Ben's choice of classes.

b) List five well-defined classes that Ben could split the clothes into.

Census Data and Sampling

Make sure you know what your population is — you can't do anything without that.

Q1 Write down the definition of the term 'population'.

Q2 Write down a definition of the term "sample frame".

A sample frame from a picture gallery...

Q3 Say what the population is for each of these surveys:

a) The health effects of smoking on 20- to 30-year-old women.

b) The number of trees in public parks in London.

c) The average number of hours British squirrels spend juggling nuts.

d) The pay of football players in the Premier League.

Q4 Use the appropriate word below to complete these sentences:

sample frame   sample   survey   census   sausage

a) A .... is when you collect data about every member of a population.

b) A .... is a small number of members from a population.

c) A .... is a list of all the members in a population.

Q5 Give two advantages of using sampling instead of a census.

You can't just choose any old population and sample frame — they have to be the <u>best choice</u> for your survey.

Q6 An environmental group is investigating the water quality in all the lakes and council-owned ponds in Nottingham.

a) What population should the environmental group use?

b) What should they use as a sample frame?

Q7 Lancashire County Council want to carry out a census of their residents to find out information such as employment, income, and size of household.

a) What is the population for this census?

b) State two problems that they might encounter while doing this.

Q8 a) Give one advantage of using census data instead of sample data.

b) 100 names are chosen at random from a telephone book.
Give one reason why this might not be an appropriate sample to use to find out about the incomes of people living in the area covered by the telephone book.

Census Data and Sampling

Q9 Professor Xavier Entric is doing a research project on
the lifespan of moorland dung beetles in the UK.

      a) What population would Professor Entric use for his research?

      b) Give one reason why Professor Entric would not use a census.

Q10 James wants to know the average weekly wage earned by teenagers in his town.
He calculates the mean from the weekly wages of three of his classmates at school.

Give two reasons why this sample may not give him
a true estimate of the average wage for the town.

Q11 Whitby football club are trying to find out about how
much their supporters are prepared to spend on merchandise.

  a) What population should Whitby football club sample from?

The football club prepare a questionnaire and send it to 1000 people
chosen at random from the electoral register of Whitby.

  b) What population have Whitby football club used as a sample frame?

  c) Give one criticism of the way that Whitby football club have chosen their sample.

Q12 A Year 11 class are collecting data about the distance that members of the teaching
staff travel to get to their school in the morning. They each survey a sample of 30
teachers chosen at random from a list of all the teachers in their school.

Here are John and Kelly's results:

John's Results

Distance travelled d (miles)	No. of people
$d < 1$	⊬⊬ ||||
$1 \leq d < 4$	⊬⊬ |
$4 \leq d < 6$	⊬⊬ |
$6 \leq d < 10$	|||
$d \geq 10$	⊬⊬ |

Kelly's Results

Distance travelled d (miles)	No. of people
$d < 1$	⊬⊬ ⊬⊬ |
$1 \leq d < 4$	⊬⊬ |||
$4 \leq d < 6$	⊬⊬
$6 \leq d < 10$	||
$d \geq 10$	||||

John and Kelly selected their samples from the same sample frame.
Explain why their tables are not identical.

Simple Random Sampling

Ducks, jam, scissors, plant pots, sausage dogs, garlic presses, remote controls are all simple random things, but they have nothing to do with simple random sampling, which is selecting things at random from a sample frame.

Q1 What does choosing something at "random" mean?

Q2 Random numbers can be generated using random number tables.
Give two other ways of generating random numbers.

Q3 Describe how you would choose a simple random sample of 500 people from a list of 4000 names.

Q4 Here's a list of places in the UK.

1. Lancaster	6. Bristol	11. Canterbury	16. Bradford
2. Birmingham	7. Glasgow	12. Cardiff	17. Bath
3. York	8. London	13. Blackpool	18. Auntie Bettie's house
4. Truro	9. Leeds	14. Norwich	19. Edinburgh
5. Manchester	10. Plymouth	15. Southampton	20. Armagh

Choose a simple random sample of 5 places using the random two-digit number list below.

12 26 04 11 01 26 04 29 09 18 13 30 07 22 18

Q5 A bakery makes 50 Battenburg cakes every day.

The quality controller tests the cakes every Friday for weight and tastiness.
She can only use a sample of 5 cakes because the cakes get eaten in the tastiness test.

a) Each week the quality controller chooses the first 5 cakes off the production line for her sample. What is wrong with this method?

b) On one Friday, all the cakes are weighed, giving the following results:

201 g	203 g	206 g	194 g	203 g	194 g	208 g	194 g
206 g	197 g	196 g	206 g	189 g	198 g	204 g	196 g
205 g	201 g	211 g	222 g	204 g	194 g	203 g	198 g
212 g	195 g	206 g	202 g	198 g	206 g	201 g	205 g
198 g	197 g	204 g	203 g	201 g	205 g	202 g	199 g

Use the random number table on the right to choose a simple random sample of 5 cake weights. Explain how you select the sample.

909	716	837	032
099	715	820	430
031	978	750	932
001	143	207	573

Stratified and Systematic Sampling

 Some tumbling rocks said "I can't get no satisfaction". But on this page there's stratisfaction, which is almost as good. And there's systematic sampling too...

Q1 Explain how you would use systematic sampling to get a sample of 500 from a telephone directory containing 20 000 names.

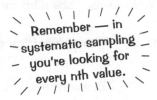
Remember — in systematic sampling you're looking for every nth value.

Q2 A company makes springs for beds and wants to perform quality control checks. Describe how it could use systematic sampling to check 100 springs from a batch of 5000.

Q3 The Instyle chain of hair salons employs 1000 people across the UK. Of these, 99 are receptionists, 53 are salon managers, 251 are colour technicians and the rest are stylists. They decide to use a stratified sample of 100 to find out about employee satisfaction.

a) How many of each type of employee should be in the sample?

b) Give one reason why it is better for the Instyle chain to use a stratified random sample than a simple random sample.

Q4 Fred is doing a statistical project on the distances travelled by students to his school.

The table below gives a breakdown of the numbers of students in each year group at Fred's school.

Year Group	7	8	9	10	11
Number of Students	398	405	401	197	199

Don't forget that the proportion of any group in a sample has to be the same as the proportion in the population.

Fred decides to take a stratified random sample with 40 students,

a) Give a reason why Fred has decided to choose a stratified sample.

b) How many Year 7 students would be in the sample?

c) In another stratified random sample from the same school, there are ten Year 11 students. How many students are in the sample altogether?

Q5 The table below shows the breakdown of staff in a large chain of restaurants.

	Waiting Staff	Bar Staff	Chefs	Managers
Male	297	199	398	49
Female	704	202	102	49

a) For an efficiency study, the restaurant management use a stratified random sample of 50 employees. They use two sets of categories.

i) How many male waiting staff should be in the sample?
ii) How many female bar staff should be in the sample?

b) In another stratified random sample with the same two sets of categories, there are 20 male chefs. How large is the sample?

Cluster, Quota and Convenience Sampling

 Cluster sampling is tricky to get your head around — it helps to remember that clusters are often based around a location e.g. districts, towns, streets etc. Quota and convenience are a bit more straightforward, thank goodness.

Q1 A large furniture shop carries out a survey to find out about the requirements of its customers. They consider two ways of getting a sample of 2000 people.

For each method, say whether cluster, quota or convenience sampling is being used:

a) The company ask a researcher to interview 2000 people visiting the shop. Of these, 500 must be aged less than 30, 500 must be 30 to 40, 500 must be 40 to 60 and 500 must be over 60.

b) The first 2000 people to enter the shop on the first Saturday in March are interviewed.

> Cluster, Quota and Convenience sampling methods are used because they're cheap as chips and easy as pie... hmmm, it must be nearly lunchtime...

Q2 Describe a method using cluster sampling to get a sample of people for a market research survey using the map of a county.

Q3 A theme park carries out a survey on which rides are the most popular.

a) Describe how they could use convenience sampling to obtain a sample of 500 people.

b) Discuss one problem the company might face in using this method of sampling.

Q4 Professor Zhargle is investigating the views of the public on scientists. First he chooses a random sample of 10 areas in a county. Then he chooses 100 men and 100 women in each town.

What two different types of sampling is Professor Zhargle using?

Q5 In the 2001 census, 390,000 people in England and Wales gave their religion as "Jedi Knight". This is 0.7% of the total population.

You are carrying out a survey which requires your sample to give a fair representation of all the stated religious beliefs in England and Wales.

How many Jedi Knights would you have to include in a sample of size 1000?

Obiwan has taught you well... but you are not a statistician yet.

Strengths and Weaknesses of Sampling

Just knowing all the different sampling methods isn't enough — you've got to be able to say what's good and bad about each method. Bring it on...

Q1 The makers of Ken and Merrie's Ice cream suspect that one of their tub-filling machines is faulty. They think that it is overfilling every fifth tub. Give one reason why it would not be useful for them to use systematic sampling to check this.

Q2 A market research company designs a questionnaire that must be answered by face-to-face interview. They choose a random sample of 2000 people using a list of households covered in the 2001 census as a sample frame.

  a) What type of sampling are they using?

  b) Give one advantage and one disadvantage of the company using this type of sampling.

Q3 The authors of a holiday guide book want to carry out a survey into the different types of accommodation in Cumbria. They select one district at random and survey all the accommodation in that district.

  a) What type of sampling have the authors used?

  b) State one problem the authors might face with their sample.

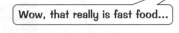
Wow, that really is fast food...

Q4 Dennis is carrying out a survey into the diet of the people who live in his town. He stands outside his local Plucky Fried Chicken fast-food restaurant and interviews the first 500 people to pass him.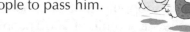

  a) What type of sampling has Dennis used?

  b) State one problem Dennis might face with the data he gets from this sample.

Q5 The headmaster of a secondary school wants to find out the views of the parents on school uniform. He thinks of two methods of selecting a sample of 50 parents:

    1 – Interview the first 50 parents to drop their children off at school in the morning.

    2 – Select the sample from a list of all parents of children at the school, making sure that the proportions from each year group are representative of the proportions in the school.

  a) Which of the two methods is most likely to give a biased sample?

  b) Give one reason for your answer to part a).

  c) What is the name given to the type of sampling used for the unbiased method?

Q6 State one problem that can arise when attempting to use stratified sampling.

Q7 **a)** Describe a situation where quota sampling rather than stratified sampling has to be used.

  b) State one disadvantage of quota sampling.

Biased Samples

 I spy with my little eye something beginning with b... If you think the answer is bias, well done, give yourself 10 points — spotting bias is what this page is all about.

Q1 Millom University Chemistry Department wants to find out the influence of its marketing on sixth-form chemistry students in the UK. They compile a survey and send it to all the students at the nearest sixth-form college.

a) Give two reasons why this sample is biased.

b) What population should the Millom University Chemistry Department be sampling from?

Q2 The Cheapeez discount food chain wants to find out what products to stock to attract more of the residents of Devon. Their interviewers survey the first 200 people to go into five Cheapeez supermarkets in Devon on the first Saturday in March.

a) Give one reason why this sample will produce biased data.

b) What population should have been sampled from?

Q3 The table below shows a breakdown of the age groups of the residents of Yeovil.

Age	Under 18	18-30	31-40	41-60	Over 60
Percentage of population	23%	17%	12%	32%	16%

The local council wants to find out whether their residents prefer to shop at out-of-town shopping centres or on Yeovil High Street. They put together a questionnaire and interview a sample of 1000 people shopping on Yeovil High Street on Saturday morning. The sample contains 205 people aged 30 or under, 421 people aged 31 to 40, 199 people aged 41 to 60 and 175 over-60s.

a) Write down two reasons why this sample is biased.

b) What population should the council have sampled from?

Q4 Four types of sampling are listed below.

> Simple random sampling   Convenience sampling
> Cluster sampling   Systematic sampling

a) Which type of sampling is most likely to produce an unbiased sample?

b) Give a reason for your answer to part a).

Q5 Fred is trying to find out why people do or don't use public transport. He surveys a sample of 100 people passing through the town bus station between 5.30 p.m. and 6.30 p.m. on a Monday evening.

a) Give one reason why Fred's sample is biased.

b) Say how Fred could improve his sample to avoid bias.

> We would like to apologise for the lack of graphic to accompany this question. We were hoping a bus might turn up.

Surveys — Questionnaires One

Questionnaires are a great way to gather information. But you need to think carefully about how you design, distribute and collect them so you get the information you want.

Q1

The Clena washing machine makers want to find out whether their customers are satisfied with their products.
They design a questionnaire which they send by post to all the people who have bought Clena washing machines in the past 12 months.
They ask people to return the completed questionnaire in the post.

State one problem which the Clena company may have when collecting data in this way.

Q2   A café owner is trying to find out which drinks his customers prefer.
He leaves a questionnaire on each table in the cafe for people to pick up.

Give one problem of distributing the questionnaire like this.

Q3 **a)** Give one advantage of using online questionnaires over paper questionnaires.

b) Give one disadvantage of using online questionnaires.

Q4   Brugton University wanted to find out what its ex-students are doing now.
It has a list of the ex-students' home addresses for the time when they were at the university.

It decided to send a questionnaire to the ex-students in the post.

a) Give one advantage and one disadvantage of distributing the questionnaire to its ex-students by post.

It asked the ex-students to send the completed questionnaire back in the post, but only 28% of the questionnaires sent out were returned.

b) Suggest two ways that they could improve the response rate.

Q5   Emma runs a one-day 'Lion Taming for Beginners' course at the local sports centre.

She hands out a feedback questionnaire at the end of the lesson and asks the students to hand the questionnaires back into the sports centre reception.

a) Give one disadvantage of distributing the questionnaire by this method.

b) Give one disadvantage of collecting the questionnaire by this method.

Q6   Peter compiles a questionnaire on music tastes and sends it to a sample of 100 students at his school. He only receives 20 questionnaires back.

Typical... well at least they were only one page late.

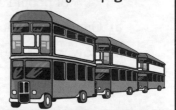

a) State one problem that Peter could have with his data.

b) What could Peter do to avoid this problem?

Surveys — Questionnaires Two

Think hard about the questions you use in a questionnaire, or it'll all go terribly wrong, and as you sob gently over your results, you'll wish you'd listened to me...

Q1　Stanley is researching the use of the school canteen.
He asks this question to a sample of students at the school:

How often do you use the canteen?　Tick one of the boxes.

Very often　☐　　*Quite often*　☐

Not very often　☐　　*Never*　☐

a) Give one criticism of Stanley's question.

b) Write a question that Stanley could use to find out how
often students at his school use the canteen.

Q2　Neeta is writing a questionnaire to find out about how students travel to her school.

a) Write one open question that Neeta could use.

b) Write one closed question that Neeta could use.

Q3　A local council wants to find out how they can attract businesses to their area.
They design a questionnaire which includes this question:

How many employees at your company watch soap operas?

Give one criticism of this question.

> Remember — questions should be easy to understand, non-leading, unbiased and unambiguous.

Q4　A drinks company is trying to profile their customers.　They want to find out which age
groups to target their marketing at.　They use this question as part of a questionnaire:

How old are you?

i)　Under 18　　　　*ii)　　18 to 30*
iii)　30 to 40　　　　*iv)　　40 to 60*

a) Give two criticisms of this question.

b) How would you improve this question?

Q5　The Milkychoc chocolate company use the following question to find out about the public's
taste in chocolate:　*Do you agree that Milkychoc chocolate is the tastiest around?*

74% of people answer yes to the question.

a) Give one reason why this has happened.

b) How would you improve the question?

Surveys — Questionnaires Three

Opinion scales and random responses are excellent ways of getting the best information from tricky questions — make sure you've learnt how to use them...

Q1　**a)** What is a pilot study?

　　b) Why is it useful to carry out a pilot study?

Q2 Give one advantage of using a question with an opinion scale instead of a yes/no question on a questionnaire.

Q3 A sixth-form college is trying to find out its students' opinions on its facilities.

a) Write a question with an opinion scale answer to find out whether the students are satisfied with the choice of books in the library.

b) Write a question with an opinion scale answer to find out whether the students are happy with the standard of the food served in the canteen.

Q4 An environmental pressure group wants to survey the people who live in Anclesfield town about their opinions on whether a new landfill site should be created.

They ask the following question:

> **Circle the response that best shows how you feel about the following statement:**
>
> **A new landfill site should be created in Anclesfield.**　**Strongly disagree/disagree/neutral/agree/strongly agree**

a) What type of opinion scale has been used in this question?

b) What other type of opinion scale could be used?

Q5 For what types of question might an interviewer use the technique of random response?

Q6 A youth group leader wants to find out what proportion of the group members smoke cigarettes. He knows that some members will not answer truthfully if he asks them whether they smoke cigarettes. Write a random response question that the leader could ask to find out the answer.

Q7 In a study on the diet of secondary school students, a health researcher asks the question:

"Do you eat one or more bars of chocolate every day?"

She knows that some students will not answer this question truthfully, so she asks them to toss a coin. If it shows heads, they tick the yes box, but if it shows tails they have to answer the question.

In a sample of 1000 students, 632 answer yes.

Use these figures to estimate what percentage of the students eat one or more bars of chocolate every day.

Surveys — Interviews

Interviews aren't just for celebs to promote their new book. You can use them to gather data too — so make sure you know their advantages and disadvantages.

Q1   Say whether each of the questions listed below is more suited for use in a face-to-face interview or in a questionnaire.

   a) What is your opinion on eating chocolate in public places?

   b) Tick the boxes which describe what you had for breakfast today. You can tick more than one box.

   ☐ Toast   ☐ Cereal   ☐ Boiled Egg

   ☐ Tea or Coffee   ☐ Fruit Juice   ☐ Other

   c) Why did you buy a house in this area?

   d) What sports do you take part in?

   e) Did you travel to work by bus this morning?

Q2   A teen magazine sends out an anonymous questionnaire which includes the following question:

   "Have you knowingly broken the law in the last twelve months?"

   Give one reason why this question would not be suitable for use in a face-to-face interview.

Not me gov'

Q4

   a) Give one reason why the question below is more suitable for use in a face-to-face interview than a questionnaire.

   "What type of food do you most enjoy when eating out?"

   b) Give two disadvantages of using face-to-face interviews to collect data rather than using paper questionnaires.

Q5   The government is carrying out a survey on income and family expenditure. They consider three methods of collecting data from a widespread sample of households:

   Method A: Send a questionnaire out by post to each household, to be returned by post.

   Method B: Devise a questionnaire and use it in a face-to-face interview.

   Method C: Devise a questionnaire and use it in a phone survey.

   a) Give two advantages of using method B instead of method A.

   b) Give two advantages of using method C instead of method B.

Observing and Recording Data

Data can be obtained by counting or measuring and recorded in a data sheet or, if you have a swish-widget-doo-hickey, you can use data logging to do both.

Q1 The following data is being collected by pupils at the Albus Academy:

> • Pupils' favourite drink at lunchtime.
> • Pupils' heights.
> • Time taken to travel to school by each pupil.
> • Weights of pupils' pencil cases.
> • Number of people living in each pupil's household.

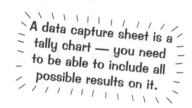

This data sheet spell needs more work — they keep coming out as bed sheets.

a) What types of data above can be obtained by counting?

b) For one of the types of data in part a) design a data capture sheet.

c) Write down an appropriate degree of accuracy for each type of data in the list that can be measured.

Q2 Mavis is collecting data about the favourite sports of the students at her school. She asks her classmates what their favourite sport is and gets the following results:

10 friends prefer football, 13 prefer rugby, 8 prefer tennis and 1 prefers BMX biking.

Design a data capture sheet based on these results for use with the whole school.

A data capture sheet is a tally chart — you need to be able to include all possible results on it.

Q3 Abbie and John are measuring fabric to make a tea towel. John suggests they measure the fabric to the nearest m and Abbie suggests the nearest cm.

a) Whose measurements should they choose? Explain your answer.

Abbie measures the fabric to be 30 cm wide and 40 cm long to the nearest cm.

b) What are the smallest and largest possible values for the actual width and length of the tea towel?

Q4 A sensor automatically measures the temperature inside a nuclear reactor every 15 minutes.

a) Name the data collection method used.

b) Say why this is an appropriate data collection method to use.

Q5 Morncrisp Cereal Company checks that their 500 g boxes of cereal are filled correctly by weighing every box of cereal manufactured.

a) Describe how data logging could be used to collect this information.

b) Why is data logging a more accurate way of recording the weights than doing it manually?

c) Other than accuracy, give one other advantage of data logging.

Experiments — Variables

 There's loads of terms you need to know for this page — the explanatory variable is the thing you change, the response variable is the thing you measure and any other variables that could affect the results are called extraneous variables.

Q1 A group of people were asked about their favourite hot drink.
The results are shown in the table.

	Under 25	25 and over
Tea	5	12
Coffee	14	12
Hot Chocolate	4	3

What are the two variables used in the table?

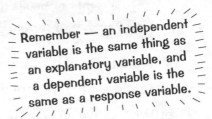 Remember — an independent variable is the same thing as an explanatory variable, and a dependent variable is the same as a response variable.

Q2 *"Listening to loud music makes people drive faster."*

a) What is the response variable for this hypothesis?

b) Write down two extraneous variables for the hypothesis in part a).

c) Why is it important to keep extraneous variables constant in an experiment?

Q3 Tess the toffee maker suspects that melted toffee flows faster when the toffee container is vibrating.

Give an example of an extraneous variable in this experiment.

Q4 Priti tests the hypothesis that schoolchildren eat more crisps as they grow older. She asks 10 children in each of the years 1, 3, 5, 7, 9 and 11 at the local schools how many packets of crisps they eat in a month.

a) What is the explanatory variable?

b) What is the response variable?

c) Write down an extraneous variable that could affect the outcome of Priti's experiment.

Q5 A scientist is investigating how springs stretch.

The results are shown in the graph.

a) What is the explanatory variable in the experiment?

b) What is the response variable in the experiment?

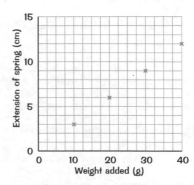

Q6 A biologist measures the effect of air humidity on rates of plant growth.

a) What is the explanatory variable?

b) What is the response variable?

c) Suggest two extraneous variables that could affect the outcome of the experiment.

Experiments — Lab, Field and Natural

 If you're doing the *AQA* course this page is especially for you. You can classify experiments depending on the amount of control you have over the variables. "What's the difference?" I hear you cry. Well if I told you, it'd be the answer to question one...

Q1 Put these three types of experiment in descending order of how much control the scientist has over any extraneous variables.

Laboratory Experiments **Natural Experiments** **Field Experiments**

Q2 Say whether each of the experiments below is a laboratory experiment, a field experiment or a natural experiment.

a) A wellie manufacturer measures average rainfall each month to see whether this has an effect on sales of wellies.

b) A teacher heats three identical beakers of water to 30 ºC, 40 ºC and 50 ºC to see whether water temperature affects the amount of sugar needed to make a saturated solution.

c) A supermarket chain collects data on whether the location of soap powder in the store affects its sales.

Q3 A psychologist investigates how age affects the way children share toys by inviting samples of children of different ages to her laboratory and observing them play with a selection of toys.

Give one disadvantage of using a laboratory experiment for this investigation.

Q4 The government wants to find out whether doing two hours or more of regular exercise per week affects academic performance at school. A random sample of new Year 11 students are given exercise diaries to complete. The sample is spilt into those who do two or more hours of exercise, and those who do less. This information is compared with the student's GCSE results at the end of the year.

a) Explain why the government cannot control the amount of exercise the students in the study do.

b) Give one reason why this experiment may not give accurate results.

She's a lovely runner...

Q5 Honest John is a car showroom manager. He asks his salespeople to use one of two sales techniques and watches CCTV footage of them in action to see which technique results in greater sales.

a) What is the name given to this type of experiment?

At Trustworthy Tim's car showroom the manager asks to be present while his salespeople try the two different sales techniques.

b) Write down one disadvantage of this method over Honest John's method.

More On Experiments and Design

There's lots of things to keep in mind when you're designing or doing an experiment — what type of experiment to use, how to keep it fair, are there any rogue values, have you got clean underwear on, that sort of thing...

Q1 What is a matched-pairs experiment?

Q2 A possible cure for the common cold is to be tested on 100 volunteers, who have all been infected with the same cold virus for the experiment.

The potential cure is in the form of a single tablet to be taken daily, and there are 730 tablets available for the experiment, which will last 14 days.

a) How many of the volunteers would you give tablets to for the two weeks of your experiment?

b) What would you do with the remaining volunteers?

c) State two variables which you would seek to keep constant throughout the experiment.

Q3 Cleo wants to investigate the hypothesis "as her fitness improves her resting heart rate will decrease". She decides to do a 20-kilometre cycle ride every day for 20 days to improve her fitness. Before each trip she uses a heart rate monitor to record her resting heart rate.

a) Why is it important that she measures her heart rate at the same time before each trip?

b) How could she improve the reliability of her results?

Q4 Amy is weighing newborn kittens to make sure they are healthy and growing properly. She records the weight of each kitten to the nearest gram and puts the data in a table:

	Week 1	Week 2	Week 3	Week 4	Week 5
Patch	110	200.8	280	368	54
Tiger	102	194	275	372	443
Felix	112	203	281	837	451

Identify any rogue values in the data and give a reason for each of your choices.

Q5 Two tennis coaches watched some matches and gave the players ratings out of 10 for their serves.

a) Explain how inter-observer bias could affect the ratings.

b) Describe how the coaches could reduce the effects of inter-observer bias.

Q6 The government wants to know how much subject knowledge gets forgotten by students over the summer holidays. A fair test is needed to test a sample of students both before and after their holidays. The table below contains before-and-after results for a group of 10 students.

Score before	88	57	69	58	74	73	59	63	60	76
Score after	75	52	58	50	65	66	48	56	54	62

a) How would you use these results to make a comparison between the students' knowledge before and after the summer holidays?

b) What conclusions could you draw from the experiment?

Simulation

Dice, dices, die, spotty cubes of chance, six-sided simulators, whatever you call them you can use them to simulate data. Woooooo.

Q1 A random number table needs to be generated for a simulation. Each number is made by using the first three significant figures of a random number produced on a calculator *(Ran# on mine)*. The first two random numbers have been put in the table for you.

a) Copy and complete the table below, using your calculator to generate the remaining random numbers.

639	225							

Random number tables are used to simulate random events happening.

b) When spun, a fair coin has an equal chance of showing heads or tails. Design a method of using the completed random number table to simulate spinning a fair coin. Explain your method carefully.

Q2 The 5-digit random number table below is to be used to simulate rolling two fair dice simultaneously. The simulated scores from each dice are to be added together for each 'roll'.

43522	41668	32142	20665	31985
76250	77071	34216	93946	34608
24155	65806	54443	13510	31415

Mel decides to use the first digit of each random number to represent the first dice, and the second digit to represent the other dice. She ignores the random number altogether if either digit is a seven or more.

a) There is another digit which makes Mel ignore a random number. What is it?

b) Copy and complete the table below for 10 simulated rolls of the pair of dice, using Mel's method.

1st Dice	4								
2nd Dice	3								
TOTAL	7								

c) Mel looks at the rolls in her table and sees that there are six threes, so states that 3 is the most likely roll. Comment on her conclusion.

d) Mel also notices that 7 is the most common total. Comment on this conclusion.

Phew, the end of the section. By now you should be a virtuoso of data collection techniques, so bring on the data analysis...

Mixed Questions

 Just what you always wanted — some questions covering different bits of Section One so you get loads of practice. Oh goody.

Q1 The head librarian of a village library wants to increase the number of people using the library by stocking titles that people want to borrow. She decides to hand out a questionnaire to find out what types of books the local residents prefer. She gives a questionnaire to everyone as they leave the library that week.

a) Is the data collected primary or secondary data?

b) i) Give two reasons why the data might be biased.

ii) Suggest one way she could have made the data more representative of the population.

Included in the questionnaire is a closed question asking how many books people borrow from the library per week.

c) i) Explain what is meant by a closed question.

ii) Give one advantage of using closed questions in a questionnaire.

Here is another of the questions in the questionnaire:

> What is your favourite type of book?
>
> Reference ☐ Fantasy ☐ Crime ☐
>
> Science Fiction ☐ Children's ☐ Romantic ☐

d) i) Give one criticism of this question.

ii) Is the data collected from this question qualitative, discrete or continuous?

Q2 A head teacher wants to find out the views of students at his school regarding school dinners. He decides to give out a questionnaire to a sample of the students.

a) Give one advantage of gathering views from a sample of students, rather than using a census.

The table below shows the total number of students in each year by gender.

	Year 7	Year 8	Year 9	Year 10	Year 11
Boys	84	89	96	99	98
Girls	92	90	94	98	102

The head teacher decides to use a sample of 75 students, stratified by year and gender.

b) i) How many students from year 11 should be included in the sample?

ii) How many year 10 girls should be included in the sample?

On a separate occasion the head teacher handed out another questionnaire to all the 200 year 11 students to find out if any of them had cheated in an exam before. They were asked to toss a coin and answer 'Yes' if it landed on heads but answer the question truthfully if the coin landed on tails. 114 students answered the question 'Yes'.

c) i) What is this technique called?

ii) Estimate how many of the students have cheated in an exam. Show your working.

Mixed Questions

Q3 Hayley, the owner of a small factory, thinks that half an hour of exercise in the morning before work would improve her employees' performance. She decides to test her hypothesis by asking her employees to exercise before they get to work and then fill in a questionnaire about their performance at the end of the day.

a) i) What would be the response variable in this experiment?

ii) Give one extraneous variable that could affect this experiment.

b) i) Why is Hayley's method flawed?

ii) How could she test her hypothesis more effectively?

Q4 The owner of a small cinema wants to investigate whether his customers would be interested in watching 3D films.

a) State the sample frame for this investigation.

He plans to survey the first 50 people who walk into the cinema on a Saturday morning.

b) i) What type of sampling is this?

ii) Give one criticism of this type of sampling.

He hands out a questionnaire to each person and asks them to put the completed questionnaire in a box at the entrance to the cinema.

c) Give one disadvantage of the owner collecting the questionnaires in this way.

Only 23% of all the questionnaires handed out are handed back in.

d) Suggest one way that the owner could increase the number of responses.

The cinema currently has four films showing.
The owner calculates the average number of people who went to see each film per day.

Film	Number of people
1	42
2	14
3	13
4	31

e) Using the random number table below, simulate which of the four films the next five people who come to the cinema are likely to see. Explain your method clearly.

586	278	607	299
537	086	668	123
233	861	951	131

Frequency Tables

Frequency tables are a good place to pick up some **REALLY EASY MARKS** — so make sure you know this stuff like the back of your hand.

Q1 Zoe plays pool in her youth club. She writes down how many of her pool balls are left on the table at the end of every game.
Here are her results:

> 3, 0, 7, 2, 1, 3, 1, 6, 4, 0, 5, 2, 0, 7, 3, 2, 1, 1, 0, 0, 0.

a) Copy and complete the frequency table below for Zoe's data.

Pool Balls	0	1	2	3	4	5	6	7
Tally								
Frequency								

b) How many games does Zoe record in total?

c) To win a game, Zoe must pot all of her seven balls and the black.
Is it possible to tell from the frequency table how many games Zoe won?

Q2 Fiona records how many birds she sees visiting her bird table each day.
Here are Fiona's results:

> 3, 8, 5, 7, 4, 3, 2, 6, 4, 7, 5, 4, 4, 6.

a) On how many days did Fiona record the number of birds?

b) What was the highest number of birds that Fiona saw visit her bird table in one day?

c) Copy and complete this frequency table for Fiona's data.

Number of birds	0	1	2	3	4	5	6	7	8	9
Tally										
Frequency										

d) What number of birds did Fiona see most often?

e) How many visits did Fiona count in total?

Grouped Frequency Tables

Grouped frequency tables are defined by classes and there are a few tricky things you need to know — Class Widths, Class Boundaries and Mid-Interval Values... So learn them all and you'll feel as happy as a kipper in a tie shop.

Q1 A group of Year 10 pupils are given 'yellis' scores. These help predict how well they will do in their GCSEs. Their teacher lists them below:

> 5.1, 6.2, 7.9, 6.0, 4.1, 5.6, 7.0, 6.8, 6.7, 5.3, 6.3, 7.2, 5.0, 5.8, 3.1.

Copy and complete this grouped frequency table:

Score (s)	Tally	Frequency
3.0<s≤3.5		
3.5<s≤4.0		
4.0<s≤4.5		
4.5<s≤5.0		
5.0<s≤5.5		
5.5<s≤6.0		
6.0<s≤6.5		
6.5<s≤7.0		
s>7.0		

Fill in the tallies first, then you can just write down the frequencies.

Q2 The ages of people in a cinema for a Saturday afternoon showing of 'Misty the Wonder Dog' are as follows:

> 85, 86, 98, 18, 12, 10, 28, 28, 29, 35, 36, 85, 86, 98
> 18, 25, 1, 2, 2, 8, 12, 10, 13, 12, 10, 11, 14, 13, 13, 10, 3, 15

Draw a suitable frequency table to show this data.
Hint: You may need to use an open-ended class.

Q3 Data about the percentage of the public in 'Speedington' who owned their own car is given in the table below:

% of people who own a car

	1980-1995	1995-2005	2005-2009
Speedington	8.8	12.7	42.2

Alex looks at the table and thinks the year classes are badly chosen. Suggest why he thinks they are bad.

Summarising and Interpreting Data

For the exam, you might need to know how to summarise bivariate data and interpret tables of real-world data. So make sure you can do these questions.

Q1 This two-way table shows the heights of fifty married couples.

a) How many couples consist of husbands who are taller than 1.9 m and wives who are taller than 1.8 m?

b) How many wives are 1.4 metres tall or less?

c) Mike says, "Tall men tend to marry tall women." Comment on whether this data supports the statement.

Men	Women		
	$h \leq 1.4$ m	$1.4 < h \leq 1.8$ m	$h > 1.8$ m
$h \leq 1.5$ m	5	2	1
$1.5 < h \leq 1.9$ m	4	17	3
$h > 1.9$ m	3	2	13

Q2 A garden centre measures the height and width of 20 begonia plants. Here are the results:

Height (cm)	20	15	10	18	12	21	13	15	17	16	22	24	12	11	9	16	14	8	11	10
Width (cm)	21	14	9	16	14	19	15	13	20	15	19	20	13	15	14	13	15	12	9	10

Draw a two-way frequency table to summarise this data.

Q3 The managers at Fruity Company Plc record the percentage of employees that eat different amounts of fruit and vegetables each day for 10 days. The table below shows the results.

	Day									
Number of portions	1	2	3	4	5	6	7	8	9	10
0	7	7	8	7	6	6	6	2	2	6
1	4	3	4	3	3	3	3	1	1	3
2	17	17	17	17	15	15	15	18	18	15
3	18	18	18	18	17	17	17	15	17	18
4	17	18	16	16	16	16	16	20	19	16
5	13	13	13	14	15	14	14	15	14	15
more than 5	24	24	24	25	28	29	29	29	29	27

a) 7% of employees ate no fruit and vegetables on day 1.
What percentage of employees ate more than 5 portions of fruit and vegetables on day 1?

b) What percentage of employees ate 3 or more portions of fruit and vegetables on day 5?

c) On day 7 the employees are given a talk on healthy eating.
How does the talk affect the percentage of employees that:
i) eat more than 4 portions of fruit and vegetables?
ii) eat less than 2 portions of fruit and vegetables?

Simplifying and Analysing Data

When you've got loads of data, it's helpful to simplify it. This will make the data easier to interpret, although you'll lose some of the original detail.

Q1 Each member of a class of 32 throws the javelin. Their distances are rounded to the **nearest metre** and summarised in the bar chart below.

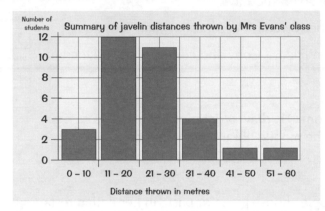

There are several ways you can simplify data — totalling, converting to percentages or grouping.

a) Copy and complete the following table, using data from the graph.

Distance (m):	0 – 10	11 – 20	21 – 30	31 – 40	41 – 50	51 – 60
Frequency	3					

b) Why might rounding to the nearest metre have distorted the data?

c) The table is simplified by using larger class widths for the distances. Copy and complete this new table:

Distance (m)	0 – 20	21 – 40	41 – 60
Frequency			

d) What important details have been lost by this simplification?

Q2 A pet shop owner has kept a record of the number of each type of animal she sold over 4 years:

Animal	2006	2007	2008	2009
Rabbits	68	90	112	120
Rats	30	28	35	36
Guinea Pigs	45	42	30	40
Stick Insects	20	18	10	9
Parrots	4	6	16	12

a) Copy and complete this new table for the total number of animals sold each year:

Year	2006	2007	2008	2009
Total				

b) What does this table show you about the total number of animals sold?

c) Now look back at the original table. What detail has been lost by totalling the data?

Bar Charts

Bar charts are nice little fellas and, if you know your stuff, can earn you some easy marks. So have a go at these...

Q1 The pictogram below shows the number of books borrowed from a mobile library over five days.

a) How many books were borrowed on Tuesday?

b) How many more books were borrowed on Wednesday than Tuesday?

c) Seven books were borrowed on Friday. Copy and complete the pictogram.

	= 2 books
Monday	📖📖📖
Tuesday	📖◗
Wednesday	📖📖📖📖
Thursday	📖📖◗
Friday	

Q2 Using the data in the pictogram from Q1, draw a dot plot of the number of books borrowed from the mobile library over the 5 days.

AQA only

Q3 Megan records how many people choose pizza or pasta in her Italian restaurant. The multiple bar chart below shows the results over one week.

a) On which days was pizza more popular with Megan's customers?

b) On which day did she have the most customers?

c) Why would it have been easier to work out part b) from a composite bar chart of the data?

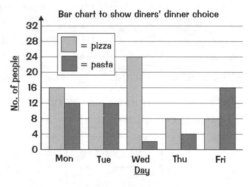

Q4 The chart below shows people's opinions about the way crime has changed in four separate years.

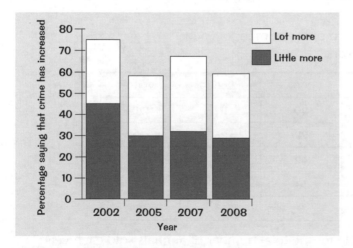

Remember — you're not always given all the information. Think carefully about the data you're given.

a) What percentage of those asked in 2005 thought that crime had increased a lot?

b) Why do none of the bars total 100%?

c) Georgi says the graph shows that fewer people in 2008 thought that crime had increased, compared to the people asked in 2002. Why might she be wrong?

Bar Charts

Q5   The chart below shows the proportion of each gender that smoke in 'Cigsville' by year.

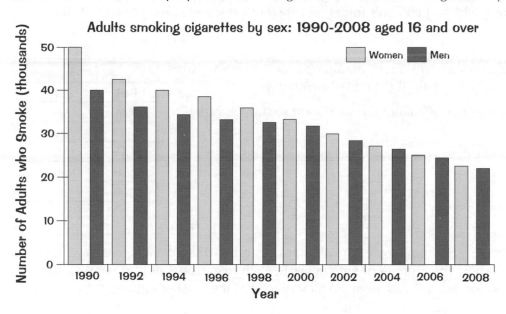

a) Describe the overall trend in smoking habits from 1990 to 2008.

b) What was the difference between the numbers of men and women smoking in 1990?

c) Describe how this difference appears to be changing over the years.

Q6   The graphs below show statistics on marital status for people over 65 years old in Knottington.

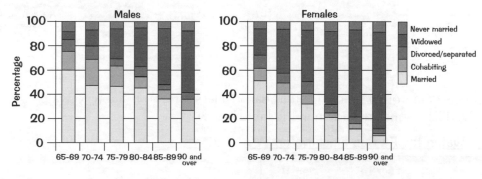

a) What proportion of males aged 65-69 are married?

b) What proportion of females aged 65-69 are married?

c) Jenny thinks that the answers to a) and b) should be the same.
     Give two reasons why she might think this.

d) She also works out that the proportion of widowed males aged 90 and over
     is about 50% and for widowed females of the same age it's about 80%.
     Give one reason which would explain such a large difference.

Pie Charts

Comparative pie charts are nasty little fellas but you still have to be able to do them (sigh) — just don't forget that they use the same area per unit of data.

Q1 The table on the right shows the number of students wearing certain coloured tops at college one Monday.

Draw a pie chart with a radius of 1.5 cm to show this data.

Colour	Frequency
Red	3
Blue	12
Green	10
Black	5
Other	15
TOTAL	45

Q2 The Sunny Shine Company has two offices, A and B. The management draw comparative pie charts to show the number of employees in each role. The radius of the pie chart for office A is 2 cm and for office B it is 3 cm. Which office has the most employees? Explain your answer.

Q3 These pie charts show the break down of total weekly spending for 50 Year 11 girls and 30 Year 11 boys.

a) What did the girls spend most of their money on?

b) If the diameter of the boys' pie chart is 3cm what is the radius of the girls' pie chart?

Note: The pie charts are not drawn to scale.

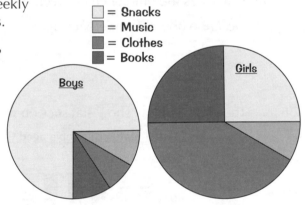

□ = Snacks
▨ = Music
▥ = Clothes
▓ = Books

Boys

Girls

Q4 Tom collects data from a Year 10 and a Year 11 class on who is likely to watch the FA Cup final live on TV. His results are shown in the table below.

Will you watch the FA Cup Final live on TV?

	Year 10	Year 11
Definitely	6	4
Very Likely	4	10
Likely	2	6
Unlikely	8	0
No Way	10	0

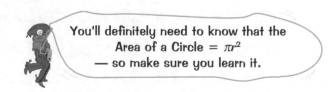

You'll definitely need to know that the Area of a Circle = πr^2 — so make sure you learn it.

Draw comparative pie charts for this data.
Draw the pie chart for Year 11 with a radius of 3 cm. Show all your workings.

Transforming Data

There is a tricky little pie chart on this page to get you thinking — make sure you brush up on angles in circles for that one...

Q1 This bar chart shows the number of sweets of different colours in a large packet. Transform this data into a pie chart. Show all of your workings.

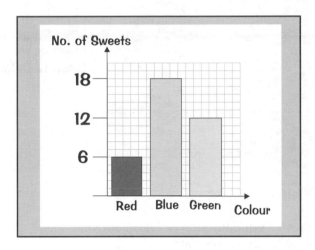

Here are three things you **MUST LEARN** about circles so that you can answer pie chart questions:

1. There are 360° in a circle.
2. The Area of a circle = πr^2.
3. Circles are round.

Q2 A newspaper asked 200 people what type of website they visited most often. The pie chart below shows the data they collected.

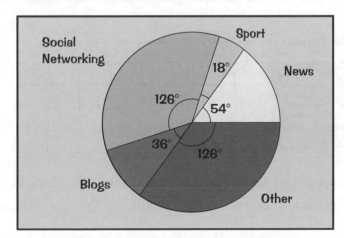

Kirsty wants to use this newspaper's data in an ICT school project, but wants to show it as a bar graph.

Transform the pie chart into a bar chart. Show all your workings.

Discrete Data and Frequency Graphs

If there's one thing you need to learn for this page, it's that the
Cumulative Frequency tells you the running total of all the frequencies.

Q1 A manager displays the number of whole days taken off sick by all members of his staff.
The data is for a two-week period and is shown in a cumulative frequency step polygon.

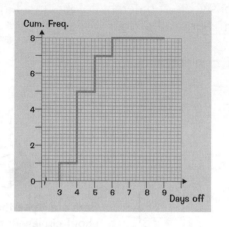

You always use
steps or lines for
Discrete Data.

a) How many people work for the manager in this office?

b) His boss doesn't understand the cumulative frequency step polygon above.
On graph paper, draw a vertical line graph to show this data.

c) How many people had 5 days off or less?

Q2 Terry is analysing the number of words in sentences in an English newspaper.
Here are his results:

> 8, 5, 6, 11, 7, 8, 7, 6, 10, 9, 5, 7, 7, 6, 6, 8, 7, 9, 7, 6.

a) Copy and complete the cumulative frequency table below.

No. of Words							
Tally							
Frequency							
Cum Frequency							

b) On graph paper, draw a cumulative frequency step polygon to show Terry's data.

c) How many sentences had 10 or less words in them?

Remember — there are easy marks for drawing
your graphs accurately and labelling your axes.

Continuous Data and Frequency Graphs

When the data you are using is continuous, like height, weight or speed, you can draw a frequency polygon or a cumulative frequency graph.

Q1 Donna works in a local butterfly house and records the wingspans of each of the butterflies in the table below.

Remember — for a frequency polygon you should plot the frequency against the midpoint of each class.

Wingspan (cm)	$0 < w \le 4$	$4 < w \le 8$	$8 < w \le 12$	$12 < w \le 16$	$16 < w \le 20$
Frequency	3	7	4	5	1

On graph paper, draw a frequency polygon for Donna's data.

Q2 Jo regularly goes out on a Friday night. Jo records her spending in the grouped frequency table below.

Remember — for a cumulative frequency graph you should plot the cumulative frequency against the upper boundary for each interval.

Jo's Spending

Spending (£)	$0 \le £ < 5$	$5 \le £ < 10$	$10 \le £ < 15$	$15 \le £ < 20$	$20 \le £ < 25$
Frequency	1	4	6	2	1

a) On graph paper, draw a cumulative frequency polygon for Jo's data.

b) Use your graph to estimate the number of times she has spent £11 or less on Friday night.

Q3 200 athletes take part in a marathon. The times taken (in minutes) for the first 50 athletes to finish the race are recorded in the groups $150 < t \le 155$, $155 < t \le 160$, $160 < t \le 165$ or $165 < t \le 170$.

The results have been plotted in the frequency polygon below.

a) How many athletes took between 160 and 165 minutes to finish the race.

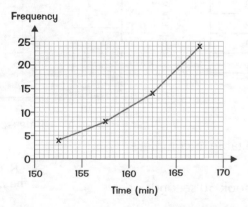

b) Use the frequency polygon to plot the cumulative frequency polygon.

c) Use your cumulative frequency graph to estimate the number of people who finished the race in less than 164 minutes.

Histograms and Frequency Distributions

 Histograms can be used to represent continuous data — now this is a bit tricky but just remember histograms can have equal or unequal class widths.

Q1 Michael conducts a survey of cars passing in one direction along his local high street on a weekday. The table below shows his results:

Time, t	08:00≤t<09:00	09:00≤t<12:00	12:00≤t<14:00	14:00≤t<15:30
Cars, n	100	90	80	75

a) Draw a histogram to represent the data. Show all your workings.

Michael then counts the number of cars from 15:30 to 16:00 and draws a bar on his histogram for this interval with a frequency density of 150 cars/hr.

b) Calculate the rate of cars passing per minute between 15:30 and 16:00.

 Behold — here is the key to all histogram questions...
Frequency density = Frequency ÷ Class Width

Q2 The table below gives some information about how long it took 16 goats to fetch a frisbee each.

Time, t (s)	Frequency
0<t≤30	3
30<t≤60	6
60<t≤70	2
70<t≤85	4
85<t≤105	1

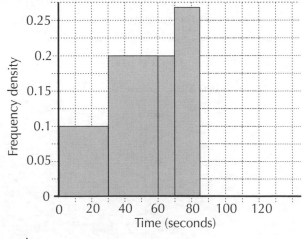

a) Use the information in the table to complete the histogram above.

b) Estimate how many goats took 50 seconds or less to fetch the frisbee.

Remember, the area of the bars is the frequency.

Histograms and Frequency Distributions

Q3   Two spinners are spun and the scores on each added together. This is done 30 times for three different pairs of spinners. The results are shown in the graphs below.

For each pair of spinners below, describe:

i)   the skew of the distribution.   **ii)** the range of total scores.

iii) the modal score.   **iv)** the median score.

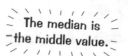
The median is the middle value.

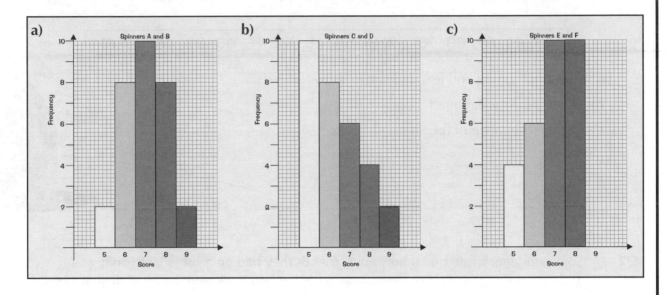

Q4   The lengths of bananas sold in a supermarket are normally distributed around the mean 18 cm. Sketch the distribution, clearly labelling the mean.

Q5   The number of people in their 50s, 60s and 70s in three villages, A, B and C, are shown in the multiple bar chart below.

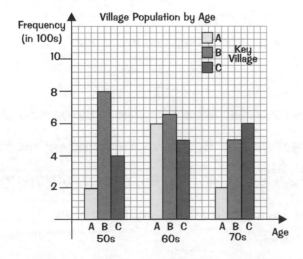

a) Calculate the number of people from each village in the survey.

b) Which village has the highest proportion of people who are in their 60s?

c) Describe the skew of the age distributions for each village.

Stem and Leaf Diagrams

Stem and leaf diagrams... everyone loves a bit of nature in their lives... remember, these can be used to show the shapes of distributions and are useful for comparing sets of data.

Q1 Jack is training his racing snail for the Mollusc World Championship 50 cm sprint. He records the training times to the nearest second in the list below:

> 48, 44, 37, 66, 70, 52, 31, 50, 45, 52, 45, 43, 32, 45, 59, 61

a) Construct a stem and leaf diagram to show Jack's data.

b) What is the modal time?

c) What is the range of the times?

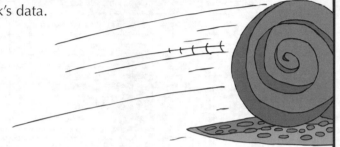

Q2 Some students wrote down how many friends they had on a social networking site. The results for girls and boys are given in the back-to-back stem and leaf diagram below.

	Girls		Boys	
Key for Girls:				**Key for Boys:**
3 | 1 = 13	7 5 4 0	0	7 8	0 | 7 = 07
	6 4 3 1	1	2 5	
	8 2 1	2	2 3 6	
	8	3	1 1 2 4 6	

a) What is the highest number of friends any of these students had?

b) What proportion of the girls had less than 10 friends?

c) What is the modal number of friends for the boys?

d) Comment on the number of friends the girls had compared to the boys.

Q3 The data below show the percentage scores achieved by a class in Biology and French tests.

> Biology: 48, 60, 50, 52, 70, 52, 31, 50, 45, 52, 45, 43, 66, 45, 59, 61, 37, 43
>
> French: 50, 44, 37, 66, 70, 52, 68, 50, 45, 52, 55, 67, 62, 85, 79, 71, 88, 76

a) Draw a back-to-back stem and leaf diagram to show the results.

b) What is the range of the scores in French?

c) What is the median score for Biology?

d) Did this class do better in the French or Biology tests? Explain your answer.

SECTION TWO — TABULATION AND REPRESENTATION

Population Pyramids and Choropleth Maps

Population pyramids and choropleth maps aren't as bad as they seem...
make sure you can <u>interpret</u> both of these for the exam... off you go.

Q1 The choropleth map below shows the population density of eight districts of a city.

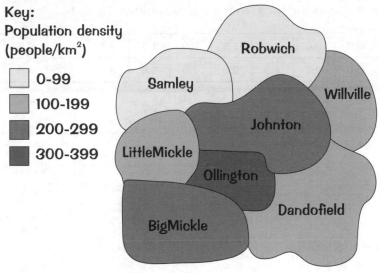

Key:
**Population density
(people/km²)**

☐ 0-99
▧ 100-199
▨ 200-299
▩ 300-399

a) Which district has the highest population density?

b) What is the population density of Bigmickle?

c) Which regions have a population density between 0-99 people/km²?

Q2 These two population pyramids compare the distribution of ages in Broughtonia and Moorland:

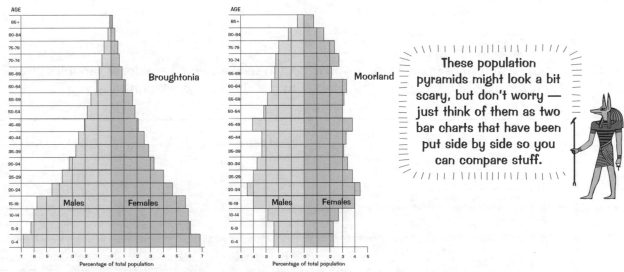

These population
pyramids might look a bit
scary, but don't worry —
just think of them as two
bar charts that have been
put side by side so you
can compare stuff.

a) What percentage of the total population in each country is aged 0-14?

b) Explain why these figures might be different.

c) **i)** What percentage of males in Moorland are over the age of 70?

ii) What is the equivalent percentage for females?

d) Explain why there is a difference between the proportions of
men and women over the age of 70 in Moorland.

e) What does Moorland's pyramid indicate about the birth rate in recent years?

Scatter Diagrams

Look carefully at scatter graphs to see if there's a relationship between the variables — if there is, you can draw a 'line of best fit'.

Q1 The scatter graph shows the data from the table below. Three points have yet to be plotted.

x	3.5	3.0	6.0	4.0	5.5	2.0	1.0	5.5	4.5	5.5	7.0
y	4.0	5.0	3.0	4.0	3.0	7.0	6.5	3.5	4.0	4.0	2.0

a) Copy and complete the graph, filling in the missing points.

b) Draw on a line of best fit.

c) Describe the relationship between *x* and *y*.

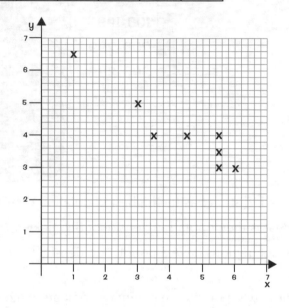

Q2 What relationships (if any) would you expect to see between the pairs of variables given below? Copy the axes and sketch the lines of best fit that show these relationships.

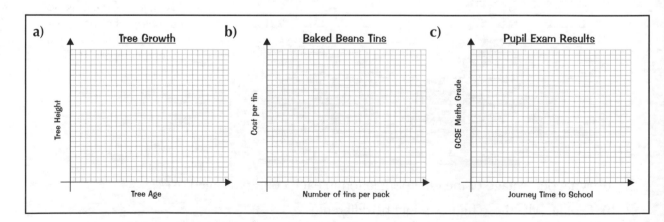

a) Tree Growth — Tree Height / Tree Age

b) Baked Beans Tins — Cost per tin / Number of tins per pack

c) Pupil Exam Results — GCSE Maths Grade / Journey Time to School

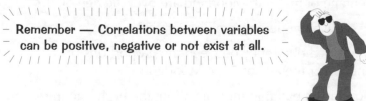

Remember — Correlations between variables can be positive, negative or not exist at all.

Time Series

Time series charts can be plotted if you have data which has been collected at regular time intervals. For example, sales figures, rainfall etc. You need to know how to <u>plot</u> them, draw a <u>trend line</u> and <u>interpret</u> them...

Q1 **a)** Time series charts sometimes show seasonal fluctuations. What does this mean?

Here are three time series charts:

i) 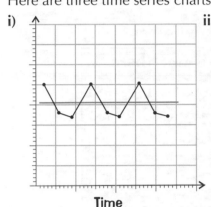 Time

ii) 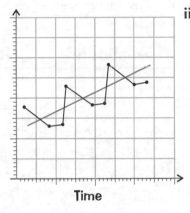 Time

iii) 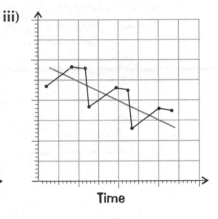 Time

b) Describe the underlying trend for each chart.

Q2 A gardener records the temperature in her greenhouse every 2 hours over a 12-hour period. Her results are shown in the table below.

	0900	1100	1300	1500	1700	1900	2100
Temperature (°C)	27	28	30	31.5	30.5	29	28

a) Draw a time series graph to show this data.

b) Comment on the trend of the data.

Q3 The table below shows the population of a village, recorded every six months for four years.

	2006	2007	2008	2009
Jan	770	710	650	620
Jul	750	670	660	580

a) Draw a time series graph to show this data and draw a trend line.

b) Comment on the trend of the data.

c) Use your trend line to predict the population in Jan 2010.

SECTION TWO — TABULATION AND REPRESENTATION

More Diagrams, Problems and Errors

Diagrams can sometimes be misleading... things can start to get really confusing when you try to do fancy things like make your bar chart 3D or paint a portrait of the Queen's face on your pie chart...

Q1 The diagram shows information about two large regions of the world.
Information includes populations, income, etc.
The key shows the value of each symbol.

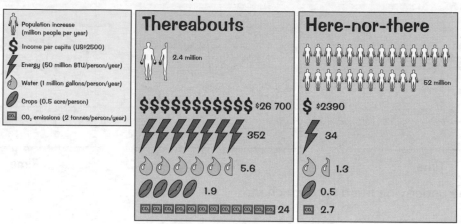

a) One lightning symbol ⚡ represents 50 million units of energy (BTU/person/year).
Do the energy diagrams appear to correctly show the energy data given?
Explain your answer.

b) Karl thinks that there is one mistake in each of the population increase diagrams.
What has Karl noticed?

Q2 The graph below shows average monthly temperatures for the months April to August.

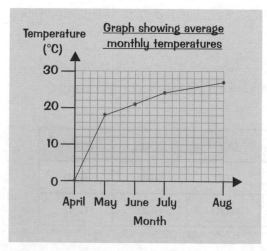

a) Jane thinks that the temperature for April has been plotted incorrectly.
Do you agree? Explain your answer.

b) The *x*-axis is unevenly scaled. What effect does this have on the graph?

More Diagrams, Problems and Errors

Q3 Fred practised taking free kicks at a target goal. In each practice, he took 100 shots. In the first practice, he hit the target 40 times. In the second practice, he hit the target 80 times. Fred draws 5 different diagrams to show how his shooting has improved.

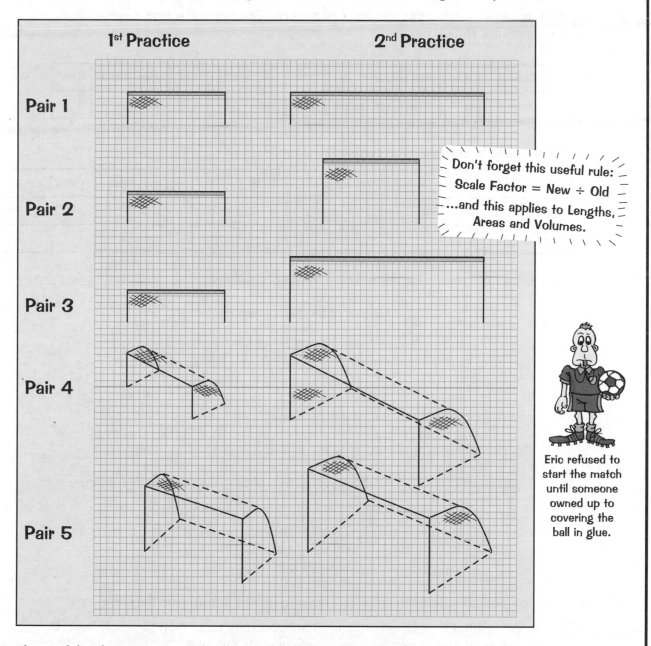

Don't forget this useful rule:
Scale Factor = New ÷ Old
...and this applies to Lengths,
Areas and Volumes.

Eric refused to start the match until someone owned up to covering the ball in glue.

a) Three of the diagrams correctly show Fred's improved shooting. Which two diagrams are misleading?

b) Explain why the diagrams which are misleading are not correct representations of Fred's practice results.

Q4 Amy's teacher reckons that Amy chats three times as much as Kayleigh. She draws a circle of radius 3 cm to represent Kayleigh's chatting. What diameter circle should she draw to represent Amy's chatting? Show your workings.

Mixed Questions

Now that you've worked through all the questions in Section Two, here are some more just for you...

Q1 Anna measures the heights (in cm) of players on two different school football teams. Her results are shown below:

Team A	176	184	198	160	181	186	173	189	189	180	186
Team B	170	179	186	168	171	169	151	177	167	177	162

a) Use this data to complete the grouped data table below.

Height, x (cm)	$150 \leq x < 160$	$160 \leq x < 170$	$170 \leq x < 180$	$180 \leq x < 190$	$190 \leq x < 200$
Team A	0	1	2	7	1
Team B					

Anna shows her results for Team A on a frequency polygon:

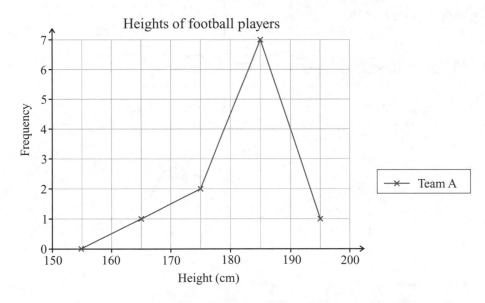

b) i) Copy and complete the graph by showing Team B's results on the same axis.

ii) Anna says that the players on Team A are generally taller than those on Team B. Explain how Anna's frequency polygon supports this view.

c) i) Copy and complete the cumulative frequency table below for Team B's results.

Height, x (cm)	$x < 160$	$x < 170$	$x < 180$	$x < 190$	$x < 200$
Cumulative Frequency					

ii) Draw a cumulative frequency polygon for Team B's results.

Mixed Questions

Q2 A group of 33 pupils were asked to estimate the length (l) of a straight line without measuring it. The actual length was 10 cm.

The results are shown below in centimetres.

10.6	12.3	9.4	11.8	11.7	8.5	9.6	14.3	11.0	12.9	8.3
10.7	12.0	10.5	11.8	12.2	8.3	9.7	7.4	13.6	9.8	10.5
8.7	9.6	7.6	10.7	12.0	7.1	8.9	11.6	12.9	10.4	11.2

a) Copy and complete this grouped frequency table:

Length (l) cm	Frequency
$6 < l \leq 8$	
$8 < l \leq 9$	
$9 < l \leq 10$	
$10 < l \leq 11$	
$11 < l \leq 12$	
$12 < l \leq 15$	
Total	33

b) State one advantage and one disadvantage of recording this data in a grouped frequency table.

c) Use the data to draw a histogram.

d) Use the histogram to estimate the number of pupils who guessed the string was 13 cm or more.

Q3 The table below gives information about the distances travelled to work by people living in the South West and North East areas of England in 2009.

Distance (d) travelled, km	South West Number of people (in thousands)	South West Angle (degrees)	North East Number of people (in thousands)	North East Angle (degrees)
$0 \leq d < 2$	952	119	1273	
$2 \leq d < 5$	624	78	608	
$5 \leq d < 10$	560	70	532	
$10 \leq d < 20$	424	53	475	
$20 \leq d < 30$	136	17	247	
$d \geq 30$	184	23	285	
Totals	2880	360	3420	360

The pie chart on the right represents the South West data.
It has a radius of 3 cm (not to scale).

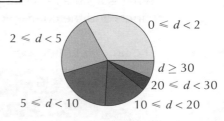

a) i) Calculate the radius of a comparative pie chart used to show the North East data, correct to one decimal place.

ii) Copy and complete the North East part of the table above, by calculating the angles to represent the North East data.

iii) Draw the pie chart to show the North East data.

b) State one similarity and one difference between the South West and North East commuters.

Mean, Median and Mode

Make sure you know the difference between MEAN, MEDIAN AND MODE, and how to work them out. You've got plenty of practice here, so get stuck in.

Q1 These are the heights in metres of twenty Year 11 students:

> 1.65 1.48 1.82 1.63 1.68 1.52 1.65 1.54 1.65 1.50
> 1.53 1.80 1.77 1.54 1.55 1.70 1.68 1.65 1.72 1.76

a) Calculate the mean.

b) What is the median?

c) What is the mode?

Q2 The mean age of Mr. and Mrs. Short and their three children is 15.
When Uncle Sam comes to stay, the mean age of the household rises to 18.

How old is Uncle Sam?

Q3 The times taken by 12 members of the Hackney Harriers to run the London marathon are recorded below:

2hr31m	2hr45m	2hr38m	2hr35m	2hr50m	2hr54m
2hr28m	2hr35m	2hr42m	2hr35m	2hr48m	2hr39m

a) Calculate the mean. *You may find it easier to take away a suitably chosen value first, but don't forget to add it back in again.*

b) Another member of the Hackney Harriers ran the London marathon in 2hr52m.
If his time is added to the list, what will happen to the mean?

Q4 Susan was copying out some data for her statistics investigation, but she couldn't read two out of six numbers. The remaining four numbers were:

7 4 6 8

She knew that the mean and the median were both equal to six.
What were the two missing numbers?

Q5 A GCSE exam consists of two question papers and a piece of coursework.
The papers carry a weight of 0.4 each and the coursework carries a weight of 0.2.
What is a student's final percentage if she scores 50%, 65% and 45% for the two papers and the coursework respectively?

Q6 The times (in minutes) taken by ten vampires to glide three miles are given below:

0.0365	0.0321	0.0365	0.0383	0.0301
0.0312	0.0363	0.0309	0.0357	0.0329

Using a suitable linear transformation calculate:

a) the mean,

b) the median,

c) the mode.

Edexcel only   Edexcel only

Edexcel only

Mean, Median and Mode — Discrete Data

If you've collected discrete data and recorded it in a frequency table, you can still analyse it by calculating the mean, median and mode.

Q1 For a set of data, $\Sigma xf = 396$ and $\Sigma f = 12$.

Calculate the mean for this data set.

Q2 The ages of a group of 30 children in a playground are given in the tally chart below:

Age	1	2	3	4	5	6
Tally	||	|||||	|||	|||||	||||| ||||	|||||	

a) What is the mean age?

b) What is the median?

c) What is the mode?

Q3 Every time Roger plays golf he keeps a record of his score on the first hole. The table below shows his last 120 scores.

Score	3	4	5	6	7	8
Frequency	2	15	38	34	23	8

a) Calculate the mean.

b) What is the median?

c) What is the mode?

Q4 A group of Year 11s were asked how many text messages they received in one week. The results are given in the table below.

Number of texts in a week	5	6	7	8	9	10	11	12	13	14	15	16
Frequency	12	10	5	24	18	8	5	20	12	3	2	1

a) Calculate the mean, median and mode.

b) Another student said that he received 30 texts in one week. Recalculate the mean, median and mode including this extra data.

46

Mean, Median and Mode — Grouped Data

Finding the three 'M's for grouped data can be a pain in the... side.
It's really important for the exam though, so practise with these questions.

Q1 One of the competitions at a fête involved guessing the number of sweets in a jar.
The guesses were recorded and tabulated:

Guess	51-70	71-90	91-110	111-130	131-150	151-170
Frequency	2	15	28	24	18	8

If you have <u>discrete</u> data that's grouped you need to take the <u>midpoint</u> of each group to estimate the mean.

a) Calculate an estimate for the mean.

b) Why is the answer to part a) only an estimate?

c) In which group is the median?

d) What is the modal class?

Don't forget the difference between <u>discrete</u> data and <u>continuous</u> data.

Q2 Eric and Bill played a darts match.
A breakdown of their scores is
shown in the table:

Score	1-30	31-60	61-90	91-120	121-150	151-180
Eric	2	34	32	5	3	1
Bill	2	47	18	6	2	1

a) Which of the mean, median and mode should you use to decide who probably won and why?

b) Who do you think won, and why?

Q3 Susan runs a 'Fat Club' and made notes for her 40 clients. She put them into groups
according to their weights. Ten were in the group $70<x\leq90$ kilograms, 16 were in the group
$90<x\leq110$ kilograms and 14 were in the group $110<x\leq140$ kilos.

a) What is an estimate for their mean weight?

b) Which is the modal group?

c) In which group is the median weight?

Q4 The heights of 50 African elephants are recorded in the table below.

Height (cm)	$270<x\leq300$	$300<x\leq330$	$330<x\leq360$	$360<x\leq390$	$390<x\leq420$
Frequency	5	22	12	8	3

a) What is an estimate for their mean height?

b) Which is the modal group?

c) Estimate the median height.

Choosing the Best Average

 Make sure you understand the differences between the mean, median and mode so that you know which one to use for a particular data set...

Q1   A manufacturer tested the lifetime of a particular type of light bulb so that he could confidently state how many hours they lasted. The results for eight such light bulbs are as follows:

| 3090 | 2400 | 2010 | 2520 | 90 | 2620 | 2800 | 2550 |

a) Which average should he use to justify his statement?

b) Which average would be the least useful, and why?

c) What should the manufacturer do to be more sure of his statement?

Q2   What one main advantage does the mode have over the mean and the median?

Q3   Give two advantages of using the median instead of the mean for a data set.

Q4   State the most appropriate average (mean, median or mode) for working out each of the following:

a) A cricketer's batting average.

b) The most popular type of music at a school.

c) The average number of people visiting a theme park every day in August, including the August Bank holiday when the theme park puts on a special event.

Averages — shedding light on your data...

Q5   The annual interest rate for the last four years on my bank account was 4%, 8%, 7% and 8% respectively. What single annual interest rate is this equal to?

Q6   If over a period of four years you are offered consecutive annual interest rates of 6%, 7%, 8% and 9% or a fixed annual interest rate of 7.5%, which should you take?

Justify your answer.

 You need to remember when it's best to use the mean, median and mode — and why...

Range, Quartiles, Deciles and Percentiles

Remember to put the data in <u>ascending</u> order before you work out where the quartiles, deciles or percentiles come in a list.

Q1 The following table shows the number of cars parked in a multi-storey car park at midday on each day in December:

690	720	580	590	210	650	640	710	700	750	790	220	790	840	830	820
900	880	480	1000	990	1020	1010	1000	80	240	370	510	460	600	580	

a) What is the range?

b) What is the lower quartile, Q_1?

c) What is the median, Q_2?

d) What is the upper quartile, Q_3?

Quartiles divide the data into 4 equal groups, deciles divide it into 10 equal groups and percentiles divide it into 100 equal groups.

Q2 The weights (in g) of 29 eggs are:

60	72	58	60	68	69	59	72	54	56	65	68	63	70	71
67	64	63	69	62	63	67	59	72	61	66	65	67	70	

a) What is the median, Q_2?

b) Which decile is equivalent to the median?

c) What is the 9th decile, D_9?

Q3 The following data shows the number of appointments not kept at the local doctor's surgery each month for the last eleven months:

38	52	18	25	32	21	42	23	29	37	24

a) What is the upper quartile?

b) What is the 5th decile?

c) What is the 50th percentile?

Q4 The range of 99 different integers is 98, and the median is 350.

a) What is the lower quartile, Q_1?

b) What is the 4th decile, D_4?

c) What is the 3rd percentile, P_3?

d) Which percentile is the number 399?

Interquartile and Interpercentile Range

Right, now for some lovely questions on estimating ranges.
I hope you're ready to plot some curves... thrilling stuff this.

Q1 For all the whole numbers from 1 to 399 inclusive:

a) What is the interquartile range?

b) What is the $P_{60} - P_{40}$ percentile range?

The interquartile range
tells you the range of the
middle 50% of the data.

Q2 The graph on the right shows the
cumulative frequency curve for the
height in cm of 200 sunflowers at
8 weeks old.

a) Estimate the median height.

b) What is the interquartile range?

c) What is the 20th percentile?

d) What is the D_1 to D_9 interdecile range?

e) Give one reason why the interdecile
range may give a more realistic idea
of the spread of the data than the
interquartile range does.

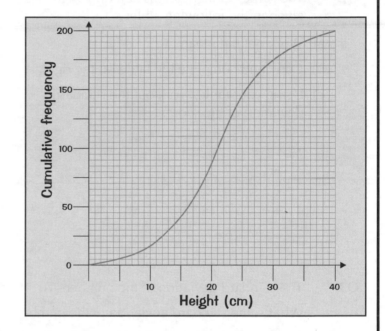

Q3 The weights (in kg) of a company's employees were taken and recorded in the table below:

Weight (kg)	Freq	Cum freq
w<50	0	0
50≤w<55	3	3
55≤w<60	8	11
60≤w<65	27	38
65≤w<70	32	70
70≤w<75	25	95
75≤w<80	29	124
80≤w<85	35	159
85≤w<90	27	186
90≤w<95	18	204
95≤w<100	6	210

a) Plot the cumulative frequency curve for the data.

b) Use your graph to find:

i) the interquartile range,   ii) the 30th percentile,

iii) the $P_{70} - P_{30}$ percentile range.

Variance and Standard Deviation

Remember that variance and standard deviation are measures of spread. To figure them out you'll need to sharpen up your calculator skills, so have a go at these questions... go on... you know you want to.

Q1   If the variance of a set of data is 1.0404, what is the standard deviation?

Q2   The scores of eight teams at a quiz night are given in the following table:

a) Work out the mean, $\bar{x}$.

b) Copy and complete the table on the right.

c) Using your table, work out the standard deviation of the scores.

x	$x-\bar{x}$	$(x-\bar{x})^2$
64		
71		
68		
79		
62		
73		
67		
64		

Q3   The standard deviation of the numbers 1 – 10 inclusive is 2.87.

What is the standard deviation of the numbers 11 – 20 inclusive?

Q4   For a set of data, $\sum x^2 = 3840$, $\bar{x} = 17.4$ and $n = 12$.

Use this information to calculate the standard deviation.

Q5   A man weighed himself on ten different makes of bathroom scales with the following results in kg:

85.8	85.9	86.0	85.7	85.9
85.8	86.1	86.0	85.8	85.9

a) Calculate the mean weight.

b) Calculate the variance and hence the standard deviation of these weights.

You need to be comfortable using the formulas for variance and standard deviation — but they'll be given to you in the exam.

Variance and Standard Deviation

Q6   For a set of data, $\sum fx^2 = 67$, $\sum f = 12$ and $\bar{x} = 2.3$.

 a)   Calculate the variance, and

 b)   the standard deviation for the data set.

Q7   The table on the right gives some information
      about a data set. Copy and complete the table
      to help you calculate:

 a)   the mean,

 b)   the variance,

 c)   the standard deviation.

x	f			
1	3			
2	5			
3	4			
4	2			
5	1			

Q8   Forty packets of crisps were sampled and the number of crisps
      in each were recorded in the frequency distribution below.

Number of crisps in packet	27	28	29	30	31	32	33	34	35
Number of packets	3	5	6	8	2	7	5	3	1

 a)   Calculate the variance and standard deviation of the data set.

 b)   Three more packets of crisps are sampled and they have 30 crisps in each.
      Recalculate the standard deviation for this data set.

Q9   The heights of 50 cheeky leprechauns were measured and the
      results are given in the grouped frequency distribution below.

Height (cm)	$30 < x \leq 40$	$40 < x \leq 50$	$50 < x \leq 60$	$60 < x \leq 70$	$70 < x \leq 80$
Frequency	9	10	13	15	3

   Use this table to estimate:

 a)   the variance,

 b)   the standard deviation.

Remember, you can find the
mean of a grouped
frequency distribution
by taking the midpoint
of the group as the x value.

Box and Whisker Plots

Hey! Pretty pictures... kind of...

Q1 Describe the skew for each of the following box plots:

a)

b)

c)

Q2 Draw a box plot using the following information:

Lowest value = 1

Range = 38

Lower quartile = 17

Upper quartile = 28

Median = 24

A <u>box and whisker plot</u>
is sometimes just called
a <u>box plot</u>.

Q3 The box and whisker plot below shows the age distribution of people in a small village.

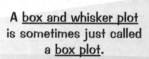

0   10   20   30   40   50   60   70   80   90
age (years)

a) Write down the median age.

b) Work out the interquartile range.

c) Describe the skew of the data set.

Q4 The scores of Wrinkly Bottom Cricket Club 1ˢᵗ XI were as follows:

| 103 | 2 | 81 | 57 | 14 | 37 | 42 | 25 | 18 | 7 | 0 |

a) What is the median?

b) Work out the interquartile range.

c) Show this data on a box plot.

d) Describe the skew of the data set.

More on Box and Whisker Plots

If you're doing *Edexcel* then skip down to question 3, for the rest I'm afraid it's from the top...

Q1 Calculate the quartile coefficient of skewness for each of the distributions shown in the box and whisker plots below. Comment on the shape of each distribution.

a)
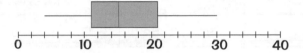

b)
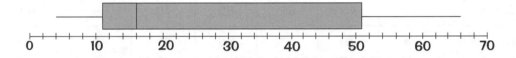

c)
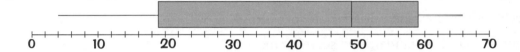

Q2 The mean score in a statistics test is 8 out of 10.
The median score is 9 out of 10. The standard deviation is 1.2.

a) Calculate Pearson's coefficient of skewness for this distribution.

b) Comment on how the scores in the test are spread.

Q3 The number of cherries on 20 cherry trees are given below.

| 25 | 26 | 58 | 30 | 35 | 27 | 40 | 37 | 24 | 34 |
| 33 | 27 | 45 | 42 | 29 | 38 | 33 | 31 | 24 | 48 |

Identify any outliers in the data given that the lower quartile for the data set is 27 and the upper quartile is 39.

Outliers are defined as any values greater than $Q_3 + 1.5(Q_3 - Q_1)$ or less than $Q_1 - 1.5(Q_3 - Q_1)$.

Q4 Below is a list of the number of text messages sent by 23 students in one week:

| 0 | 8 | 10 | 11 | 12 | 13 | 15 | 17 | 24 | 24 | 25 | 26 |
| 28 | 32 | 32 | 34 | 37 | 37 | 50 | 55 | 70 | 79 | 88 |

a) Draw a box plot to show this data.

b) Identify any outliers in the data.

c) Redraw the box plot taking these outliers into account.

The Normal Distribution and Standardised Scores

Learn all about standardised scores and the normal distribution before you try this page...

Q1 The table below shows the percentages gained in exams for 5 students along with the mean and standard deviation for the whole class.

Subject	Amy	Bob	Carla	David	Edward	Mean	Standard Deviation
History	45	72	61	39	54	47	8
Geography	69	47	52	58	49	51	5.5
Music	75	40	59	52	70	58	6.1
Maths	44	38	49	82	57	55	6.7
English	57	44	53	63	40	54	4.9

a) What is Carla's standardised score for history?

b) What is David's standardised score for music?

c) In which subject did Amy give her best performance?

d) What is Edward's total standardised score?

e) In which subject did Bob give his worst performance?

Don't forget the <u>simple formula</u> for working out standardised scores.

Q2 A wedding cake company finds the amount of sugar used each week is normally distributed with a mean of 1000 kg and a standard deviation of 100 kg.

How much sugar would you advise them to have available per week so that they could be almost certain they'll never run out?

Q3 Laura and Jane's marks for Information Technology and German are recorded in the table below, along with the mean and standard deviation for the whole class.

	Laura	Jane	Mean	Standard deviation
I.T.	54	48	46	12
German	40	46	44	18

a) Gill noticed that she had the same standardised score for German as Jane had for I.T. What mark did she get?

b) Who did better overall, Laura or Jane?

Q4 The weights of packets of SoggyFlakes cereal are normally distributed with a mean of 500 g. However, 2.5% of the packets weigh less than 485 g.

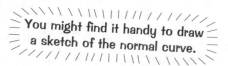

You might find it handy to draw a sketch of the normal curve.

Work out an estimate for the standard deviation of the weights of the packets.

Comparing Data Sets

You can use measures of location and spread to compare data sets.

Q1 The four box plots show the spread of mark adjustments made by the team leader to the sample scripts of four examiners, A, B, C and D.

a) Which examiner is the most reliable? Explain your answer.

b) Which examiner is the most unreliable? Give a reason for your answer.

c) What advice would you give to examiner D to improve their marking?

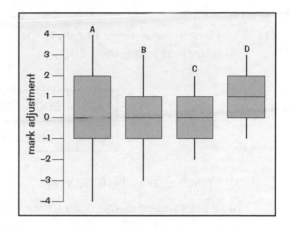

Q2 A summary of two batsmen's scores for a cricket season is shown in the table on the right.

Answer the following questions, giving a reason for each choice.

a) Which batsman was the most consistent?

b) If both batsmen were out for a duck (scored 0) at least once, which batsman had the highest score?

c) Which batsman had the best batting average?

	A	B
Mean	48	65
Median	47	51
Range	164	130
Standard Deviation	29	24

Q3 The employees of a company usually travel to work by car or by bike. The box plot below shows the journey times (in minutes) for those who travel by car.

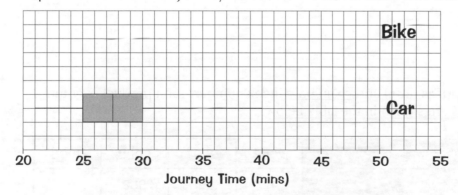

The table gives information about the journey times (in minutes) for employees who cycle to work.

	Minimum	Q_1	Q_2	Q_3	Maximum
Bike	33	37	43	45	48

a) Copy the grid above and use this data to draw a box plot to show the distribution of bike times.

b) Comment on two differences between the distributions.

Summary Statistics

You've got to know all about simple index numbers and chain base index numbers (they're really useful if your data includes prices) — so enjoy. ☺

Q1 Here are the index numbers for the price of a particular model of car since it was launched in the year 2005:

Year	2005	2006	2007	2008
Index	100	108	112	114

a) Which year is the base year?

b) If the car first came onto the market for £26 000, what was the price of the car in 2007?

c) If, instead, the price of the car in 2007 was £29 400, what would the car have been sold for in 2008?

AQA only

Q2 Last year the number of deaths in Wentwell was 432.
If Wentwell had a population of 28 600, what was the crude death rate last year?

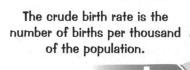

The crude birth rate is the number of births per thousand of the population.

AQA only

Q3 The crude birth rate in Bournville in 2008 was 21.4.
If the population in 2008 was 15 000, how many babies were born that year?

Q4 Some of the prices (in £) and <u>chain base</u> index numbers for a product over the last four years are shown in the table below.

Year	2006	2007	2008	2009
Price (£)	750	825	858	
Chain base index number				95

a) Copy and complete the table.

b) What does the chain base index number for 2007 show?

c) Using 2006 as the base year, calculate the index number for 2009.

Summary Statistics

Q5 The makers of a brand of Yorkshire pudding use a batter mix containing milk, eggs and flour. The company wants to calculate a weighted index number for the ingredients to help them work out how their costs are rising.

Their spending on ingredients for 2008 and 2009, along with the products' weights (the percentage of the budget spent on them), are shown below:

	2008	2009	Weight
Milk	£8.70	£9.90	28
Eggs	£14.40	£15.60	47
Flour	£7.80	£8.70	25

a) Calculate the index number for:

   i) the milk

   ii) the eggs

   iii) the flour.

> You need to remember the nice and simple <u>formula</u> for the weighted index number.

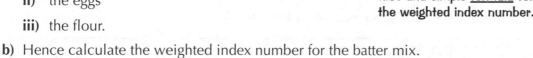

b) Hence calculate the weighted index number for the batter mix.

c) What does this say about the company's spending on ingredients in 2009 compared to that in 2008?

Q6 The value of a piece of land increased over a two-year period, as shown:

Year	2007	2008	2009
Value (£)	25 000	30 000	32 000

a) Using 2007 as a base year, calculate the index numbers for the years 2008 and 2009.

b) By what percentage did the value of the land increase between 2007 and 2009?

Q7 The age distribution for the towns Hadham and Lostham are given in the table below:

Age Group	Hadham %	Lostham %
0 – 15	12	3
16 – 30	33	19
31 – 45	37	25
46 – 60	15	33
over 60	3	20

a) Which town is likely to have a higher crude birth rate?

b) Is the standardised birth rate for Hadham likely to be higher or lower than its crude birth rate?

c) Why would a standardised birth rate allow you to compare the birth rates in these towns more fairly?

Time Series

Time series graphs can be really useful if you want to make predictions for the future. But first it's best to plot moving averages to make your trend line more accurate.

Q1 For each of the following sets of data, calculate:

a) 3-point moving averages:

| 60, | 65, | 55, | 57, | 63, | 55, | 62, | 60, | 58 |

b) 7-point moving averages:

| 10, 12, 13, 8, 3, 11, 10, 10, 11, 13, 9, 7, 5, 2 |

Q2 The table below shows sales at a bakery over three weeks.

Week	1					2					3				
Day	M	Tu	W	Th	F	M	Tu	W	Th	F	M	Tu	W	Th	F
Sales (£)	100	130	120	80	110	105	135	130	90	110	110	140	140	100	115

a) Calculate 5-point moving averages for the data.

b) Plot the moving averages and draw a trend line through the points.

Q3 A shoe shop recorded the total number of pairs of shoes sold every 3 months from January 2007 to December 2009. The information is recorded in the table below.

	Jan-Mar	Apr-Jun	Jul-Sep	Oct-Dec
2007	2150	2270	1950	2480
2008	2850	2820	2780	3110
2009	3250	2950	3300	3440

a) Draw a time series graph to show this data and draw on a trend line. Use the trend line to predict the number of pairs of shoes sold between Jan and Mar 2010.

b) Calculate and plot a 4-point moving average for this data on the same graph.

c) Use these moving averages to draw a line of best fit and use this to predict the number of pairs of shoes sold in the period Jan-Mar 2010.

d) Which answer is the most reliable, a) or c)?

Time Series

Q4 The takings in a bed and breakfast by the sea are largely dependent on the weather.
The takings (in £) in 2007 to 2009 are shown in the table below.

	Jan-Mar	Apr-Jun	Jul-Sep	Oct-Dec
2007	2600	4200	10 500	5000
2008	3000	5500	16 000	4800
2009	3400	6100	20 000	5400

a) Plot the data on a time series graph.

b) Calculate and plot the appropriate moving point averages.

c) Draw a trend line for the moving averages.

d) What is the seasonal effect for Jan-Mar 2008?

e) What is the average seasonal effect for Jan-Mar?

Moving averages help you plot trend lines more accurately.

Q5 A tutor records his income from private tuition over each quarter.
His results are shown in the table below.

	2006	2007	2008
Jan – Mar	2800	3010	3380
Apr – Jun	2230	2550	2820
Jul – Sep	1350	1620	1900
Oct – Dec	2560	2820	3280

private tuition = cha-ching

a) Draw a time series graph to show this data.

b) Calculate and plot a 4-point moving average on the same graph.

c) Draw a trend line using your moving averages.

d) What is the seasonal effect for Jul-Sep 2007?

e) Calculate the average seasonal effect for Oct-Dec.

f) Use the trend line and the average seasonal effect to predict the tutor's private income for Oct-Dec 2009.

More Types of Time Series

This page is for **AQA** only. There are two more types of time series you need to know about — z charts and output gap charts. So on your marks, get set, go...

Q1 Here is an output gap chart for the small state of Richenstein:

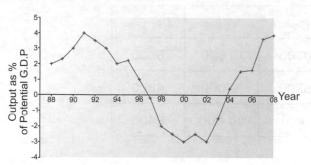

a) Describe the state of the Richenstein economy between 2004 and 2008.

b) What happens to prices of goods in a boom?

c) Explain why unemployment started to rise in Richenstein in 1997.

Q2 This z chart shows how many mangos were sold by a greengrocer during 2009.

a) How many mangos were sold in June 2009?

b) What were the total mango sales between the start of 2009 and May 2009?

c) What were the total mango sales in the 12 months up to February 2009?

d) Comment on the popularity of mangos in 2009 compared to the year before.

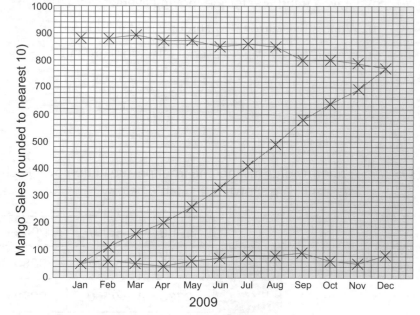

Q3 A college collects average attendances for each half term in 2008 and 2009 in order to draw a z chart.

a) Copy and complete the table below.

	2008						2009					
	Autumn		Spring		Summer		Autumn		Spring		Summer	
Half Term	1	2	1	2	1	2	1	2	1	2	1	2
Attendance	91	87	81	81	90	91	96	92	88	88	94	93
Total since Autumn 2009 half term 1							96	188	276	364	458	
Total for the past year							526	531	538		549	

b) Use your table from part a) to draw a z chart for the data.

c) The principal of the college started a strategy to improve attendance during 2008. Has the strategy been successful? Explain your answer.

Quality Assurance

Quality assurance is important to make sure products turn out okay.
The quality of products can be checked by taking samples and calculating certain statistics.

Q1   A manufacturer checks that the waist sizes of skirts being produced are the required 60 cm.
A sample mean is taken every two hours and the results recorded below.

	0900	1100	1300	1500	1700
Mon	60	61	60	59	60
Tue	59	60	61	59	61
Wed	60	60.5	61	62	62

a) Plot each day's averages against the time.

b) Should any action be taken and if so, when and why?

Q2   A coffee machine is checked every day for a week. A sample of the same number
of cups is taken every morning and the range of the sample's fill level is recorded.
The acceptable range is 1 cm.

Day	Mon	Tue	Wed	Thu	Fri	Sat	Sun
Level (cm)	1.0	0.9	0.7	0.9	0.5	1.0	0.8

a) Plot these ranges against the time.

b) Should the owner of the coffee machine have taken any action? Justify your answer.

Q3   There should be on average 20 matches in a box. Every 30 minutes a sample of 3 boxes is taken
and the mean number of matches in the sample is calculated for quality assurance purposes.

The graph on the right shows
the results over four hours.

For each of the sample
numbers state if any action
should have been taken,
what type of action, and why.

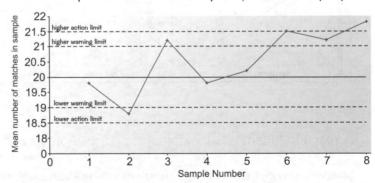

Q4   Three machines are used to make 55 cm long shoe laces. Samples are taken regularly
from each machine and their mean length recorded below.

	1000	1100	1200	1300	1400	1500
Machine A	55	55	54	55	56	55
Machine B	55	54	55	56	53	58
Machine C	54	55	56	57	58	58

a) Plot each machine's sample means against the time.

b) Is machine A working properly? If not, why not?

c) Should any action be taken on machine B?

d) Is machine C okay? Give a reason for your answer.

If some of the averages
are way out, then
there are problems...

Correlation

Two variables can be positively correlated, negatively correlated or not correlated at all.

Q1   What does correlation mean?

Q2   For each pair of variables below, state what type of correlation
you'd expect if you plotted them against each other.

   a) Outside temperature, number of visitors to the zoo

   b) Age, number of pets

   c) Number of hours spent on homework, number of hours spent watching television

   d) Shoe size, life expectancy

   e) Hours of sunshine, time spent in the garden

Q3   Describe the correlation shown by the following graphs.
(Make sure you answer in terms of the variables involved).

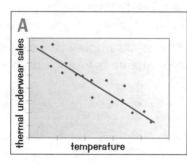
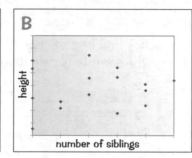
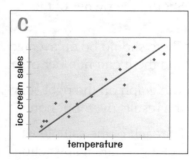

AQA only

Q4   A Year 11 student was looking at the correlation between the number of friends on a
social networking site someone had and the number of event invitations they received.
She worked out the product moment correlation coefficient to be 0.75.

Comment on what this value means.
(Remember to relate your answer to the variables in the question.)

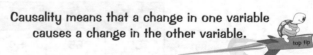
Causality means that a change in one variable
causes a change in the other variable.

Q5   State which of the following pairs of variables, if any, have a causal link.

   a) Sales of DVDs and sales of chocolate

   b) Speed of car, stopping distance

   c) Temperature outside, heating bills

   d) GCSE Mathematics score, GCSE History score

Correlation

The following questions refer to the scatter diagrams below:

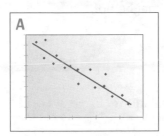 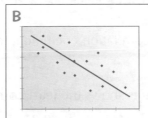 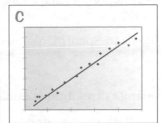 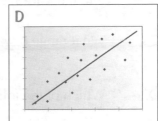

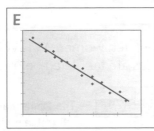 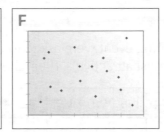 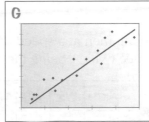

Q6 State which of the scatter diagrams above have:

a) strong positive correlation

b) no correlation

c) weak negative correlation

d) moderate positive correlation

e) moderate negative correlation

f) weak positive correlation

g) strong negative correlation

Q7 Below are four pairs of variables that relate to the scatter diagrams B, C, D and F. Which diagram is most likely to relate to each pair?

a) The force with which a ball is hit, the distance it travels

b) Time spent on computer, time spent watching television

c) Shoe size, money in bank account

d) Waist size, hat size

Q8 Ollie counted how many raisins and marshmallows he could fit in his mouth all at once. The table shows his results from 12 tries.

Number of raisins	190	100	220	290	260	30	150	270	30	140	70	240
Number of marshmallows	13	15	10	3	8	24	14	5	20	19	22	7

Using a suitable scale, draw a scatter graph to show the data. Plot the number of raisins on the *x*-axis and the number of marshmallows on the *y*-axis. What type of correlation does the graph show?

Spearman's Rank Correlation Coefficient

 If you've got ranked data then you can use Spearman's rank correlation coefficient to measure the correlation between variables... sounds ace... erm maybe not.

Q1 What range of values can Spearman's rank correlation coefficient take?

Q2 Which of the following correlation coefficients shows the least correlation?

   0.9   0.15   −0.8   −0.1   0.95   0.4

Q3 Two young men at a speed dating event were asked to rank ten women, W1–W10, in order of preference (with 1 being the most attractive). Their choices are tabulated below:

	W1	W2	W3	W4	W5	W6	W7	W8	W9	W10
Romeo	5	6	3	2	9	1	8	10	7	4
Casanova	2	6	1	4	10	3	9	8	5	7

 The Spearman's rank formula's given to you in the exam, so you can look it up if you need to.

Top Tips

a) Calculate Spearman's rank correlation coefficient for this data.

b) Do Romeo and Casanova have similar tastes in women?

Q4 Judges Benchley and Court awarded marks to seven competitors, C1–C7, taking part in a gymnastics competition. These are shown in the table below:

	C1	C2	C3	C4	C5	C6	C7
Judge Benchley	8.7	9.4	8.0	9.2	7.6	9.0	8.8
Judge Court	8.9	9.5	8.2	9.0	7.7	9.1	8.7

a) Work out Spearman's rank correlation coefficient for this data.

b) How similar are the judges' rankings?

Q5 Two friends at a wine tasting were asked to award marks out of ten for eight different wines, A–H. Their scores are shown in this table:

	A	B	C	D	E	F	G	H
Thelma	6	5	2	6	7	9	4	7
Louise	7	6	10	4	3	1	8	2

a) Copy and complete the table below to show how the two girls ranked each wine.

	A	B	C	D	E	F	G	H
Thelma					2.5	1		2.5
Louise			1					

b) Use these ranks to calculate Spearman's Rank Correlation Coefficient.

c) What does this tell you about their tastes in wine?

Working with Scatter Diagrams

The line of best fit should run as close to as many of the points on the scatter diagram as possible. Ideally, it should go through the mean of both variables.

Q1 The table below shows the ages of a sample of boys and the number of packets of crisps they eat in an average week.

Age	10	7	12	16	13	12	15	11	8	15
Packets of crisps	3	10	1	5	12	7	8	4	2	3

a) Plot this data on a scatter diagram.

b) Is there any correlation? If so, draw a line of best fit.

Q2 The diagram below shows the correlation between the results of two mathematics papers for a group of students.

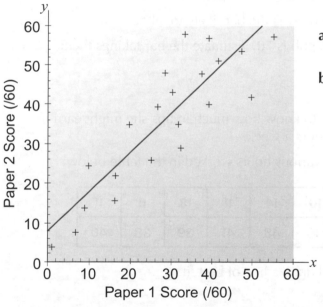

a) Work out the equation of the line of best fit shown.

b) What does the equation of the line of best fit tell you about the relative performance of the students in the two papers?

Q3 A van driver wanted to know if the load he carried affected the van's diesel consumption, so he recorded the details for several long trips he made:

Load (tonnes)	0.5	2.6	7.0	2.8	5.0	7.2	6.0	1.3	3.6	4.4
Miles per litre	6.9	6.3	4.3	5.9	5.2	4.6	5.0	6.7	5.9	5.6

a) Plot the data on a scatter diagram and draw a line of best fit.

b) Is there any correlation? What does this mean?

c) Work out the equation of this line.

d) What does the *y*-intercept tell you about the van's diesel consumption?

Interpolation and Extrapolation

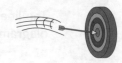

You can use scatter diagrams to predict unknown values, so have a go with these questions...

Q1 **a)** Define the term "interpolation".

  b) Which is more likely to give you an accurate estimate — interpolation or extrapolation? Explain your answer.

Q2 The number of tickets sold and the associated bar takings for some pub gigs are tabulated below:

Number of tickets sold	45	68	24	38	57	63	60
Bar takings (£)	340	560	150	290	510	600	550

  a) Plot this data on a scatter diagram and draw a line of best fit.

  b) If just 30 tickets are sold, how much money is the bar likely to take?

  c) The maximum capacity allowed in the pub is 70. Estimate the bar takings then.

Q3 Julia, a part-time waitress, was curious to know how much in tips she might earn if she turned full-time, and worked 38 hours a week.

  She recorded the tips she received for various hours worked in the table below:

Hours worked	10	8	12	10	14	11	13	11	11
Tips (£)	40	33	42	38	48	41	39	38	40

  a) Plot this data on a scatter diagram and draw a line of best fit.

  b) Find the equation of the line of best fit.

  c) Estimate, by using this equation, how much in tips Julia could hope to receive working full-time.

  d) How accurate would you expect her estimate to be? Explain your answer.

Extrapolation is when you predict a value outside the range of the data set.

Estimation of Population

A lot of populations are too big, or too hard to track down, to be able to do a census. So you can use samples to make estimates about a population.

Q1 Hazel has a large number of slugs in her garden. To find out what type of slug they are, she needs to know their lengths. She measures ten slugs in total, with the following results:

| 12 cm | 14 cm | 12.5 cm | 11.5 cm | 13.5 cm |
| 13 cm | 12 cm | 10 cm | 11 cm | 13 cm |

a) Use Hazel's measurements to estimate the mean length of the slugs in her garden.

b) How or why might this result be inaccurate?

Q2 A farmer has 30 equally populated henhouses. He collected and counted the eggs from six of these houses on the same day, with the following results:

| 37 | 42 | 35 | 47 | 42 | 37 |

a) How many eggs, on average, does each of these henhouses yield?

b) How many eggs would the farmer expect to get altogether each day?

Q3 Name an accurate (and practical) way of estimating the size of a population of wild deer.

Q4 Some students at Braggleton University conducted an opinion poll to find out if their fellow students approved of top-up fees. They asked 100 students from each of four year groups. The results are tabulated below.

	Yes	No	Don't know
1st Years	10	80	10
2nd Years	15	80	5
3rd Years	25	50	25
4th Years	30	20	50

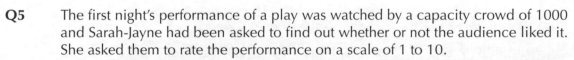

A sample needs to be big enough to accurately represent the population.

a) Based on the data in the table, estimate what percentage of students agreed with the introduction of top-up fees.

b) How could this estimate have been improved?

c) What do the majority of students think?

Q5 The first night's performance of a play was watched by a capacity crowd of 1000 and Sarah-Jayne had been asked to find out whether or not the audience liked it. She asked them to rate the performance on a scale of 1 to 10.

Which of the following would be a suitable sample size to form a realistic public opinion?

a) **i)** 5   **ii)** 300   **iii)** 50

b) Sarah-Jayne finds her results are quite variable and is worried that they may not be an accurate estimate of what the whole audience think of the play. What sample size should she use to halve the variability of her results?

SECTION THREE — DATA ANALYSIS

Capture / Recapture Method

When you use the capture and recapture method to estimate population sizes, you've got to be careful about the sample you use — make sure you know all about it...

Q1 A large lake in a public park needs to be emptied and dredged of silt.
The council want to find out how many fish live in the lake.

One afternoon volunteers net and mark 112 fish, then safely return them to the lake.
A few hours later, the volunteers net 30 fish and find that 12 of these are marked.

a) What assumptions do you have to make to use the capture / recapture method for finding out population sizes?

b) Calculate the number of fish that the council might expect to be in the lake.
Show your working clearly.

Q2 An environmental health officer wants to know how many rats and mice live in London's sewers. On one visit, she captures and tags 70 rats and 30 mice before setting them free. The following visit she captures 50 rats and 50 mice and finds that 2 rats and 3 mice are tagged.

a) How many rats would the environmental health officer predict live in the sewers?

b) How many mice can she expect there to be?

Q3 Eaton Forest is full of foxes and chickens. To try and find out how many of each were in the forest, 20 foxes and 50 chickens were caught, tagged and released. At the end of each of the next three weeks a number of each were caught, checked and released, with the following results:

	1st week		2nd week		3rd week	
	Caught	Found tagged	Caught	Found tagged	Caught	Found tagged
Foxes	24	4	22	3	18	2
Chickens	40	1	30	2	30	3

a) Based on the first recapture, how many foxes and chickens were there?

b) Assuming the number of tagged animals in the population remains constant over the three weeks of the study:
i) estimate how many foxes and chickens there were at the end of the 2nd week,
ii) estimate how many chickens there were by the end of the third week.

Q4 Below is a list of populations:

i)	Flies in a field	iv)	Trees in a wood
ii)	Sheep in a field	v)	Bacteria in a Petri dish
iii)	Tadpoles in a pond		

a) For each population, state whether capture / recapture could be used to estimate the population sizes.

b) If capture / recapture can't be used for any of the populations, state the reasons why.

Mixed Questions

If you still have loads of topics from Section Three swimming round your head then you can put them to good use by trying these mixed questions.

Q1 120 people were asked how long, on average, they spend reading the Sunday newspaper. The cumulative frequency graph below shows the results.

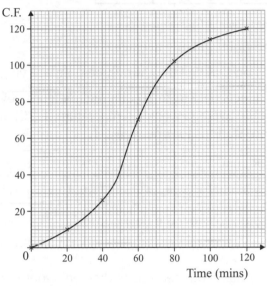

a) Use the graph to estimate the median time taken reading the Sunday newspaper.

b) Estimate the D_2 to D_8 range for this data.

Q2 The members of Scoresdale Sports Club go out each weekend to try different sports. One week they went karting at a local circuit and recorded all their lap times. Dave's lap times were 67, 64, 112, 69, 74, and 71 seconds. He wants to find his average lap time.

a) Suggest a suitable average he could use. Explain your answer.

The range of Dave's lap times was 48 seconds.

b) i) Give one criticism of using the range as a measure of spread for this data.

ii) Suggest an alternative measure of spread that would be more suitable. Explain your answer.

The next week the club went to a dry ski slope and noted their times on a slalom course. The table below shows the fastest karting lap time and slalom run for each member.

	Karting time (sec)	Skiing time (sec)	Karting rank	Skiing rank		
Anna	56	65	3			
Becca	62	62	4			
Chaz	51	60	1			
Dave	64	58	5			
Eric	53	59	2			

c) Copy the table above and complete the rank column for skiing.

d) Calculate the Spearman's rank correlation coefficient for karting against skiing. You can use the blank columns in your table for your working.

e) Use your answer to part d) to comment on the relationship between the times for the two sports.

Mixed Questions

Q3 A meteorology station records temperature, T (°C), to an accuracy of one tenth of a degree at the same time on consecutive days.

Day	1	2	3	4	5
T (°C)	5.4	6.2	4.0	4.8	x

The first three-point moving average is 5.2 °C.

a) Calculate the next three-point moving average.

b) Find the temperature, x, on Day 5 if the third three-point moving average is 4.8 °C.

A weather forecaster collects data from 10 different meteorology stations.
The table below shows the average weekly temperature, T (°C) and the total weekly rainfall, R (mm), for each of these stations for one week.

Total weekly rainfall, R (mm)	14	7	21	10	8	15	18	23	14	16
Average weekly temperature, T (°C)	13.4	15.7	11.0	16.2	14.3	14.8	12.5	9.8	11.2	14.1

c) i) Draw a scatter diagram to show the data above.

ii) Draw a line of best fit on the scatter diagram and describe the correlation shown.

Q4 The Green Beenz factory has produced tins of different types of beans for 30 years. Each day a sample of tins of green beans is taken at regular intervals and weighed. The range of the sample weights is recorded. The acceptable range is 3 g.

a) Give one reason why the weights of the tins are checked.

The graph below shows the sample ranges for one day last week.

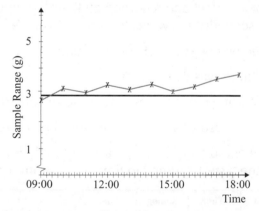

b) Should any action have been taken in the production process? Explain your answer.

The Green Beenz factory also produces tins of butter beans. Samples of these are also weighed at regular intervals. It has been found that the mean weight of the samples is 418 g, with a standard deviation of 0.7 g. The mean weights are normally distributed.

c) Between what limits would you expect 95% of the sample mean weights to lie?

The factory finds that the weight of butter beans it produces each day has a mean of 1000 kg and a standard deviation of 90 kg.

d) One year the factory operates for 300 days. On how many of these days would you expect the weight of butter beans produced to be less than 820 kg?

SECTION THREE — DATA ANALYSIS

Probability One

Remember: the probability of any event happening must lie between 0 and 1
— the more likely an event is to happen, the closer its probability will be to 1.
If you get a bit confused, try drawing a scale like the one below.

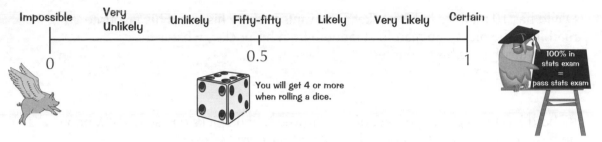

Q1   What is the definition of the term "event"?

Q2   Draw a probability scale from 0 to 1, labelling the points 0, 0.1, 0.2, ..., 1.
Mark points a, b and c on your scale to show how likely you think each of these events is:

   a) A van that is less than a year old will break down in the next year.

   b) A van that is 50 years old will break down in the next year.

   c) A van that is 10 years old will break down in the next year.

Q3   Christina says that she has a probability of 1.4 of passing her GCSE Statistics exam.
Explain why this isn't possible.

Q4   Two goats, Glenda and Gertrude, have a sprint race. If both goats finish the race,
there are three possible outcomes. What are they?

Q5 **a)** For each of these spinners, decide the following:

   i) Which number is most likely to be spun.

   ii) Which number is least likely to be spun.

1.   2.   3.   4.

   b) Draw a spinner with nine sections where each number is equally likely to be spun.

Q6   Louise and Gordon both want to go to Alton Towers. They can only afford one ticket.
They decide to throw a standard dice to see who should go.

   a) What are the possible outcomes when rolling the dice?

   b) Gordon decides that if a 1, 2, 3 or 4 is thrown, he gets the ticket. Is this fair?
Explain your answer.

   c) Explain how they could use the dice to decide fairly.

Probability Two

These probability questions can be a tricky business. All you're really
interested in is the number of ways an event can happen, compared to the
total number of things that can happen. Remember that — and you're sorted.

Q1   David has 10 marbles in his pocket. He wants to show his friend his favourite
marble. If he picks one marble at random from his pocket, what is the
probability that it's his favourite?

Q2   Richard has been given a packet of mixed sweets. If he picks one sweet at random,
he has a probability of 0.25 of picking a mint-flavoured sweet.

How many sweets are in the packet if there are seven mint-flavoured sweets?

Q3   Dorothy throws a standard dice. What is the probability that she will get:

a) an odd number?

b) 2?

c) an even number?

d) a prime number?

Q4   24 runners taking part in a marathon all have an equal probability of winning.
Eight are women, and 16 are wearing tracksuits.

a) What is the probability of a woman winning the race?

b) What is the probability of a person wearing a tracksuit winning the race?

c) What is the probability of a man winning the race?

Q5   The managers of a ski resort are trying to improve the safety of the resort.
Last month 50% of those reporting an injury were between 18 and 24 years old,
36% were between 25 and 50 years old and the rest were over 50.

Assuming the above figures represent a typical week, answer this question:

What's the probability of someone who reports an injury being between 25 and 50 years old?

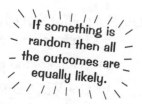
If something is random then all the outcomes are equally likely.

Q6   In a lottery 50 balls are numbered 1 to 50. A single ball is chosen at
random and the person with a ticket that matches that number wins.

a) What is the probability of the ball being an odd number?

b) What is the probability of the ball being greater than 30?

c) Jane buys a ticket for 5 different balls. What is the probability she will win?

Sample Space Diagrams

All these lovely diagrams — it's almost like art. And they're useful too.
Diagrams make it much easier to work out probabilities as they show all the
possible outcomes. So it might help to draw one even if you're not asked to.

Q1 Draw a sample space diagram to show all the possible outcomes of throwing
a standard dice *and* spinning this spinner:

Q2 Draw a Cartesian grid to show all the possible outcomes of selecting a suit from
a pack of cards *and* picking a counter from a bag containing one green counter,
one blue counter and one red counter.

Q3 Roy has started to draw a Cartesian grid to work out the possible outcomes
of throwing a standard green dice and a standard yellow dice.

a) Copy and complete the grid to show all possible outcomes.

b) Write down the probability of:

i) getting two odd numbers,

ii) getting a total of less than 8,

iii) getting two numbers whose difference is 3.

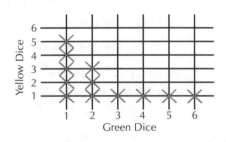

Q4 A group of children on an outdoor pursuits course are given a choice of events to try.
The results of who wants to do what are shown below:

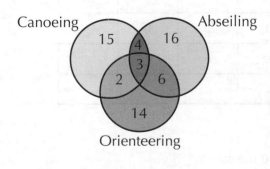

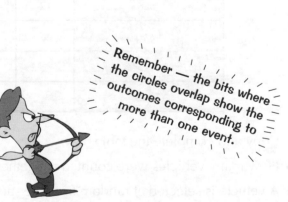

Remember — the bits where
the circles overlap show the
outcomes corresponding to
more than one event.

a) How many are in the group?

b) How many want to do canoeing?

c) i) If you picked a child from the group at random, what is the probability of him or
her wanting to do all three activities?

ii) What is the probability of the child only wanting to do orienteering?

Sample Space Diagrams

Q5 A group of OAPs went to the beach for a day trip. The Venn diagram shows how many wore a hat, sunglasses, both or neither.

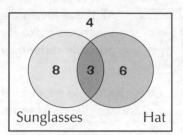

a) How many OAPs went on the trip?

b) What's the probability that a randomly selected OAP is:

   i) wearing neither a hat nor sunglasses?

   ii) not wearing a hat?

Q6 In a survey, 27 workers in an office were asked if they liked chocolate digestives, cookies or ginger biscuits. One person didn't like any of the biscuits (weirdo). Some of the results are shown in the Venn diagram below.

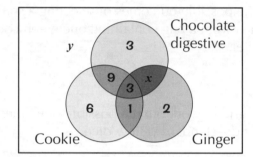

a) What are the values of x and y that should be used to complete the diagram?

b) What is the probability that a worker, chosen at random, likes ginger biscuits?

c) What is the probability that a worker, chosen at random, likes cookies and chocolate digestives, but not ginger biscuits?

Q7 A two-way table showing the results of a traffic survey is shown below.

Type of vehicle	Red	Blue	Green	White	Total
Car	12	12		3	32
Lorry	2	1	0	11	
Motorbike		2	0	1	4
Total					

a) Copy and complete the table.

b) How many vehicles were counted altogether in the survey?

c) A vehicle is selected at random from the survey. Find the probability that the vehicle is:

   i) a red lorry

   ii) a car

   iii) a green motorbike

   iv) blue

Relative Frequency

Relative frequency is all about using trials to estimate the probability of something happening next. E.g. if I've had to make eight out of the last ten cups of tea for the office, will I have to make the next one? Grumble grumble grumble...

Q1 Of the first 308 people to enter a music gig, 71 were aged 18 to 21, 157 were aged 22 to 30, and 80 were over 30.

From this data, what is the relative frequency of people aged 18 to 21?

Q2 A shop sells green and red umbrellas. The owner is trying to work out the probability that the next brolly he sells will be green, not red. He records the number of green brollies and the number of red brollies he sells in a week.

red	red	green	red	green	red
green	green	green	green	red	red
green	red	red	green	red	green

Estimate the probability of him selling a green brolly next.

Derek decided that it doesn't matter what colour brolly you have in a thunderstorm.

Q3 Simon thinks the spinner below is biased towards the number one. He spins the spinner 50 times and records the number of times it lands on one in the first 10, 20 and 50 spins in the table below.

Number of spins	10	20	50
Number of 1s spun	3	6	13
Relative frequency			

a) Copy and complete the table.

b) From this table what is the best estimate of the probability of spinning a one?

c) Is the spinner biased towards the number one?

d) Explain your answer to part c).

Q4 A six-sided dice is thrown 100 times and 45 fours are recorded.

a) Calculate the relative frequency of fours.

b) Do you think the dice is biased? Explain your answer.

Remember — biased means some numbers are more likely to come up than others.

Q5 Dana and Sunil both support Foxfield Utd. The team are currently bottom of their league after winning only 5 out of 20 games this season.

a) Estimate the probability of the team winning a game.

b) There are 16 games left to play. Dana thinks they will win 3 of them, and Sunil thinks they will win 10. Who do you think is more likely to be right? Explain your answer.

Expected and Actual Frequencies

You can predict the expected frequency of an outcome in a certain number of trials if you know the probability of that outcome occurring. But the actual frequency you get if you do the trials might be slightly different. Exciting stuff.

Q1 A standard dice is thrown 50 times. What is the expected frequency of:

a) numbers less than 4?

b) factors of 6?

c) a 5 being thrown?

Q2 A factory produces chocolate penguins which have a 5% probability of being misshapen, and boxes of chocolate frogs which have a 10% probability of failing a quality check.

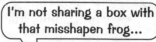

I'm not sharing a box with that misshapen frog...

a) The factory produces 280 chocolate penguins in an hour. What is the expected number of misshapen penguins produced per hour?

b) 100 boxes of frogs are checked for quality each day. How many boxes would you expect to pass the quality check each day?

Q3 Mike and his friends are brilliant at pub quizzes. For any quiz they enter, there are three possible outcomes — they win, finish second, or finish third or worse. The outcomes have probabilities 0.7, 0.2 and 0.1 respectively. This month they will enter 10 pub quizzes.

a) Copy and complete this table showing the expected frequencies of each outcome:

Outcome	First	Second	Third or worse
Expected Frequency	10 × 0.7 = 7		

b) This table shows the results of the quizzes.

Quiz	1	2	3	4	5	6	7	8	9	10
Outcome	1st	1st	1st	2nd	1st	1st	1st	1st	1st	1st

Draw a graph comparing the expected frequencies with the actual frequencies.

Q4 A crisp manufacturer claims that one in every five packets of crisps has an instant-win prize in it.

a) Out of sixty packets of crisps, how many packets would you expect to contain a prize?

Archie decides to test the claim and buys five packets of crisps.
He doesn't win in any of them and concludes the manufacturer's claim must be false.

b) Is Archie's conclusion correct? Explain your answer.

c) How could Archie test the manufacturer's claim more accurately?

Probability Laws One

The first thing to think about when tackling one of these questions is whether the events can happen at the same time — then you know which addition law to use.

Q1 State whether the following pairs of events are mutually exclusive.

a) When picking a card at random from a standard pack of cards: 'getting a heart' and 'getting an ace'.

b) 'Winning the National Lotto' and 'not winning the National Lotto' with the same set of numbers in the same draw.

c) When selecting a person at random from a group of joggers: 'getting a man with black trainers' and 'getting a man with white shorts'.

d) When throwing a dice: 'getting a 6' and 'getting a 4'.

This picture has nothing to do with these questions, but it made me chuckle.

Q2 Daphne has a box of crisps that contains 3 packets of cheese and onion, 5 packets of roast chicken and 4 packets of salt and vinegar.

Daphne selects a packet from the box at random. Find the probability that she gets:

a) cheese and onion

b) roast chicken

c) cheese and onion or salt & vinegar

Q3 George uses the spinner below to decide which kind of film to see. Each section represents a different film, and they each fall into one of three mutually exclusive categories. 'A' means he'll see an action film, 'C' a comedy, and 'S' means science fiction.

Find the probability that the film he selects is:

a) a comedy

b) action or a comedy

c) neither action nor comedy

Q4 Carolyn picks a card at random from a standard pack of 52 cards.

a) What is the probability of Carolyn getting a club or getting a heart or getting a spade?

b) What is the probability of Carolyn not getting a 5?

c) Calculate the probability of Carolyn picking a heart or a number less than 4. *Treat an ace as having a value of 1.*

d) Calculate the probability of Carolyn selecting a jack or a spade.

Q5 Alicia and Ben enter a raffle. There is a single prize, which will be awarded to the person who owns the selected ticket. Of the 50 tickets available, Alicia buys 30 and Ben buys 20.

Calculate the probabilities of each winning the raffle. Are these events exhaustive? Explain your answer.

Probability Laws Two

There's always one rule for one and one rule for another, isn't there? Events which have no effect on each other are independent, which means you can multiply the probabilities to find out how likely they are to happen together.

Q1   If you pick one card from each of three separate decks, what's the probability that you will end up with three Kings?

Q2   'Malcolm's Car Sales' have a new car to be won. All you need to do is throw a 6 seven times in a row with a standard dice.

Calculate the probability of winning the car.

Q3   Gillian is designing a new school sweatshirt. She selects a colour by putting the names of five colours (green, red, blue, burgundy and black) in a bag and randomly selecting one. She then tosses a coin to decide whether the sweatshirt should be round-necked or V-necked.

Calculate the probability of Gillian choosing:

a) a green round-necked sweatshirt

b) a black V-necked sweatshirt

c) a red sweatshirt with any neckline.

Q4   Jack, Chloe and Sophie want to order either takeaway pizza or curry for their dinner. The probabilities of each of them choosing pizza are 0.4, 0.7 and 0.1 respectively.

If these probabilities are independent find the probability that:

a) Jack will order pizza, Chloe will order pizza and Sophie will order curry.

b) all three will order curry.

Q5   Dave is baking cakes. The probability of him leaving a cake in the oven too long is always 0.15.

If he bakes six cakes, what is the probability that he forgets about at least one of the cakes?

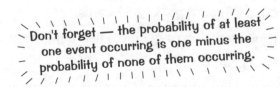

Don't forget — the probability of at least one event occurring is one minus the probability of none of them occurring.

Q6   The probabilities that Katie and Daniel will go to France this summer are 0.6 and 0.3 respectively. Assuming that these probabilities are independent, find the probability that:

a) they will both get to France.

b) only one of them will get there.

c) neither Katie nor Daniel will go to France this summer.

Tree Diagrams

Tree diagrams are really useful for working out probabilities. They're likely to come up in the exam, so make sure you can do them. Don't forget — you can easily check your diagrams by making sure that the end results add up to 1.

Q1 From the tree diagram shown, calculate the probability of passing both History and French.

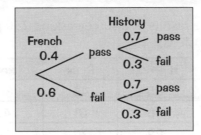

Q2 Gemma is watching a soap omnibus on a Sunday.
There are three episodes on.
The probability of her watching any one episode is 0.4.

a) Copy and complete this tree diagram:

b) Find the probability of her watching all three episodes.

c) Find the probability of her watching the first two episodes and not the third.

d) Find the probability of her watching any two episodes.

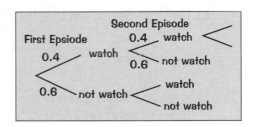

Q3 There are ten cars in a race each numbered one to ten.
Cars one, two, three and four are red and the rest are blue.

a) Draw a tree diagram to show the probability that a randomly chosen car:
- is red or blue,
- has an odd or even number.

b) Find the probability that a car picked at random is:
  i) blue and has an odd number.
  ii) red and has an even number.

Q4 The Greys and the Blues play two football matches.
The tree diagram below shows the probabilities of different outcomes
(Greys win, Blues win, or the match is a draw) for each of the matches.

a) Calculate the probability that the Blues will win both the matches.

b) What is the probability that one team will win both of the matches?

c) Calculate the probability that the teams will draw in one or both of the matches.

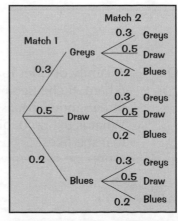

Conditional Probability

Millom
Home   Top tip

A conditional probability question is not a question you only have to answer if certain conditions are met. Oh no. It's when the probability of something happening depends on the outcome of something else.

Q1 This table shows the results of a survey asking 230 people what their favourite type of music is:

I prefer classical, hip-hop makes my hips pop.

	Hip-Hop	Rock	Pop	Total
Male	35	45	30	110
Female	48	31	41	120
Total	83	76	71	230

What is the probability that a randomly chosen person from the survey:

a) is male given that they prefer pop music.

b) likes hip-hop given that they are female.

Q2 A survey was carried out to find out what types of sport people watch on the TV. The Venn diagram shows the results.

a) What's the probability of someone watching cricket given that they watch football?

b) What's the probability of someone watching football and cricket given that they watch athletics?

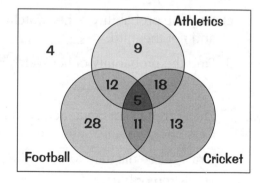

Q3 A glass jar contains 25 pink balls, 5 white balls, 17 green balls and 13 blue balls.

a) Two balls are picked at random and are not replaced.

   i) Find the probability of the first ball being pink.

   ii) Find the probability of a white ball followed by a green ball.

b) If three balls are picked from the jar and not replaced, calculate the probability that the first ball picked is blue, followed by two white balls.

Q4 A family decides to go for a picnic. There are a mixture of sandwiches: 6 ham, 8 cheese and 11 peanut butter. Each person randomly receives three sandwiches, starting with the daughter who only likes ham. What is the probability that she will get three sandwiches that she likes?

Conditional Probability

Q5 There are two sets of traffic lights on the way into town. The probability that you have to stop at the first set is 0.6. The probability that you have to stop at the second set is 0.6 if you stopped at the first set, or 0.7 otherwise.

    a) Draw a tree diagram to show the probabilities for both sets of lights.

    b) Find the probability of getting through both sets of lights without stopping.

Q6 Matt and Simon play each other twice at tennis. The probability that Matt wins the first match is 0.7. If he wins the first match, the probability he wins the second is 0.5. If he loses the first match, the probability of him winning the second is 0.8.

    a) Draw a tree diagram to show the probabilities for both matches.

    b) Find the probability that Simon wins both matches.

    c) What's the probability that they win one match each?

Q7 Joe has six white socks, twelve black socks and two blue ones.
He chooses two socks at random from his drawer, without replacing the first one.

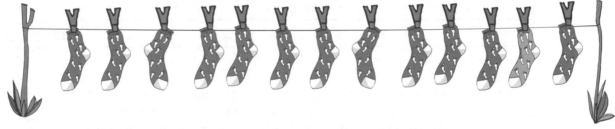

    a) Draw a tree diagram to show the probabilities for choosing two socks.

    b) If the first sock is blue what is the probability that he will get an identical pair?

    c) If the first sock is black, what's the probability that he will get an odd pair of socks. *It might be easier to use the "at least one rule" to work this out.*

Q8 The probability of it raining in the Lake District on a particular day is 0.6. If it rains on that day, the probability of it raining on the next day as well is 0.86, otherwise it's 0.54.

    a) Draw a tree diagram to show the probability of rain for the two days.

    b) If it rains on the first day, what's the probability of it not raining on the second day?

    c) Given that its not raining today what's the probability that it was raining yesterday?

Q9 A toaster is four times more likely to burn toast if it's just been used than at other times.
The probability of it burning toast if it hasn't just been used is 0.12. The probability of the toaster having just been used is 0.6.

Given that the toaster burnt some toast, what's the probability it had just been used.

Discrete Probability Distributions

If you're doing the *Edexcel* course you get to have fun with the binomial distribution on this page. If you get one of these questions in the exam and the number of trials is three or more they'll give you the expansion. Nice examiners.

Q1 A lottery machine contains balls numbered from 1 to 14. One ball is selected at random from this machine. What distribution could be used to model the ball generated by the machine in the next lottery draw?

Q2 Write down the expansion of $(p + q)^2$.

You'll need this table of binomial expansions for questions two to four.

Number of Trials (n)	Expansion of $(p + q)^n$
3	$p^3 + 3p^2q + 3pq^2 + q^3$
4	$p^4 + 4p^3q + 6p^2q^2 + 4pq^3 + q^4$
5	$p^5 + 5p^4q + 10p^3q^2 + 10p^2q^3 + 5pq^4 + q^5$

Uh oh...

Q3 The probability of a biased coin landing on heads is p, and the probability of it landing on tails is q. Using the table of expansions above, find an expression for the probability that the coin lands on heads 3 times out of 4.

Q4 Marge is eating grapes from a very large sack (you can assume that each pick is independent of the previous one). Each time she chooses a grape from the bag, there is a 15% chance that it will be damaged.

  a) What is the probability that she will find exactly one damaged grape amongst the first three she chooses?

  b) Marge chooses 5 grapes from the sack. What is the probability that exactly two of them are damaged?

Q5 At a garden centre, you can buy mixed bags of bulbs containing daffodils and tulips. When the bags are packed, each bulb is chosen at random with the probability of choosing a daffodil being 0.75 and the probability of choosing a tulip being 0.25. Each choice is independent of the previous one.

  a) Out of a bag containing three bulbs in total, find the probability of two of them being tulips.

  b) If a gardener buys a bag with four bulbs altogether, what is the probability that he gets exactly three times as many daffodils as tulips?

  c) If a bag contains five bulbs, find the probability of it containing more tulips than daffodils.

Mixed Questions

You need to be able to deal with probability questions that test you on lots of different things in the same question. So have a bash at these and you'll be sorted.

Q1 The probability of Arun getting up late in the morning is 0.5.
If he gets up late, the probability that he will arrive late for work is 0.85.
If he gets up on time, the probability of him being late for work is 0.2.

a) Draw a tree diagram to show the probability of Arun being late for work.

b) Calculate the probability that:

i) Arun gets up on time and gets to work on time.

ii) Arun is late for work.

iii) Arun got up late given that he is late for work.

Q2 Cathy throws a ball repeatedly to Rob. Rob has to try and catch it with alternate hands. Cathy throws the ball 90 times to each of Rob's hands and records whether he catches or drops it. The results are shown in the table below.

	Left hand	Right hand
Caught		76
Dropped	64	
Total		90

a) Copy and complete the two-way table.

b) Estimate the probability of Rob:

i) catching the ball, given that he was trying to catch it in his left hand.

ii) dropping the ball, given that he was trying to catch the ball in his right hand.

c) Using the results of all 180 throws, calculate the relative frequency of Rob:

i) catching the ball.

ii) dropping the ball.

d) Cathy and Rob decide to play the same game again.
What is the expected frequency of catches made if the total number of throws is 70?

Q3 A hotel serves either a full English breakfast or a continental breakfast.
Out of a total of thirty people staying one night, twenty-four ordered the full English breakfast.

a) Calculate the relative frequency of a full English breakfast.

A B&B also offers the choice of a full English or continental breakfast. The probability of a guest at the B&B ordering a full English breakfast is 0.74. The total number of guests ordering a full English breakfast can be modelled using a binomial distribution.

b) On a particular morning two people at the B&B have breakfast.
Calculate the probability that the B&B will have to serve exactly one full English breakfast.

Mixed Questions

Q4 In a typical one-month period 98.2% of all trains arriving in a station are on time.
The probability of a train arriving on time does not depend on what happens to any other train.

a) What is the expected frequency of late trains next month, when 348 trains will run?

b) Calculate the probability that at least one train is late out of four arriving in the station.

The probability of a train being late can be modelled using the binomial distribution.

c) Calculate the probability of two of the first five trains arriving at the station late.
You may use $(p + q)^5 = p^5 + 5p^4q + 10p^3q^2 + 10p^2q^3 + 5pq^4 + q^5$

Q5 People living in a village were asked what kind of material they regularly recycled.
The results are shown in the Venn diagram below.

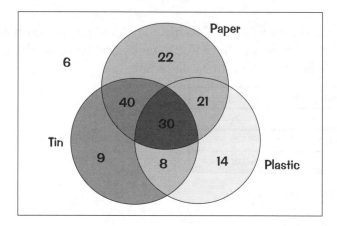

a) How many people were included in the survey?

b) A person is selected at random. What is the probability that they:

i) recycle paper?

ii) recycle plastic given that they recycle tin?

iii) recycle tin given that they recycle paper and plastic?

Q6 Alex draws a card from a standard deck.

a) Calculate the probability that the card is red or has a value more than 10.
You can assume that an ace is worth 1.
Hint: remember a card can be red and have a value of more than 10.

Alex draws two cards from the deck and does not replace the first card.

b) What is the probability of him drawing two black cards?

c) What is the probability of him drawing a pair (two cards with the same value)?